VOLUME
18

Originally published in the United Kingdom in weekly parts **COMBAT & SURVIVAL** is a study of the armed forces at work. It shows the skills taught to soldiers and the way in which military units operate. It examines the weapons and equipment used by different armies; and, by looking at recruit training and exercises, **COMBAT & SURVIVAL** demonstrates how the armed forces develop individual responsibility, leadership and initiative.

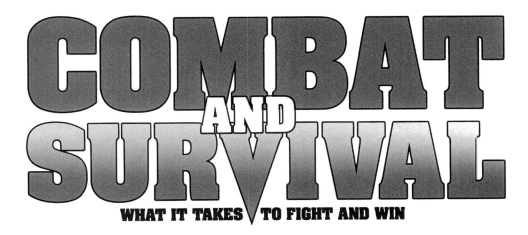

COMBAT AND SURVIVAL

WHAT IT TAKES TO FIGHT AND WIN

VOLUME
18

H. S. STUTTMAN, INC. *publishers*   Westport, Connecticut 06889

Contents

Volume 18

Published by H. S. STUTTMAN INC.
Westport, Connecticut 06889
© Aerospace Publishing 1991
ISBN 0-87475-560-3

2P(1833)20-50

DEFENDING A HOUSE

When you're defending a position, one of your first priorities is to make it as difficult as possible for the enemy to get close to you.
You do this in two ways – by the sheer weight of fire you pour in to his advancing troops, and by putting obstacles in his way. They will slow him down, and make his attack more difficult and dangerous by forcing him to follow the routes you choose. In this section on urban combat you'll learn about the kind of obstacles US infantrymen use to defend towns and cities.

Obstacles fall into two main categories: those designed to stop soldiers on foot; and larger, more substantial con-

You will not be able to occupy every house in a defended locality, so make sure that the unoccupied ones are of no use to the enemy. You do this by demolishing them or filling with command-detonated charges and mines. In training, you can simulate this by setting fire to the building!

DRESS AND EQUIPMENT

1. Equipment must be kept to a minimum so you can move freely inside the house through mouseholes and trapdoors. But you must carry your respirator, water and the maximum amount of ammunition.
2. Assault vests are superior to skeleton-order webbing as the weight is distributed more evenly and they will not catch when crawling through holes.
3. A good pair of ear defenders is vital. Try to buy a set that cuts out gunfire noise but enables you to hear a normal voice.
4. Sew knee and elbow pads into your FIBUA combats and soak them in water before the action starts.
5. Wear your helmet and plastic goggles to protect your eyes from dust and flying masonry chips.
6. Carry extra shell dressings and morphine.

structions to stop vehicles, from jeeps right up to heavy armour.

Anti-personnel obstacles are lighter, – barricades and barbed wire are the most common – but that doesn't mean that they're quicker to build. Out of doors, wire is usually used together with a variety of explosive mines, to create an obstacle in depth. Mines are particularly useful because they are difficult to neutralise: apart from being scattered over a wide area, they can cost lives to discover and remove.

Where the minefield can be covered by machine-gun and small-arms fire, it can be difficult indeed for an enemy to make progress through it without taking a lot of casualties.

Where to put wire

As with any other defensive position, it's very important to choose the site carefully. A barbed wire and mine obstacle is no use whatsoever if the oncoming enemy forces can just go round it!

Choose places like road junctions and narrow streets hemmed in by buildings, but don't forget to deal with the buildings themselves, too. Coiled wire filling a room is a very difficult obstacle to deal with. Because there's not much substance to it, it can survive explosive demolition charges remarkably well.

If the enemy can't get a vehicle up to the wire and pull large chunks of it away, he's probably left with no

The enemy will use harassing fire from mortars throughout the depth of your position to restrict your movement, inflict casualties and isolate forward objectives from reinforcement.

Rolls of wire should be fixed at the base of all external walls of the house, secured with six-foot pickets. This will stop the enemy putting pole charges against it. The wire must be at least two rolls thick.

option but to cut it out a piece at a time – not a very attractive job if he's under fire at the same time. If it's booby-trapped as well, then the job is well-nigh impossible.

This coiled-up barbed wire (known as 'concertina wire') is quite easy to handle when you're laying it. It comes in coils, secured together. But once the wrappings are released it springs out into a sort of fence, one that is as deep as it is high. And this isn't the sort of barbed wire you see down on the farm, keeping cattle from straying.

Instead of rather blunt spikes it has razor-sharp blades that will cut through even thick gloves in moments. Confronted by three or four

PREPARING A HOUSE FOR DEFENC

There is no end to the tasks that will improve your defence: the only limiting factor will be time. After you have worked out your arcs of fire and cut firing ports to cover these, you will have to work out a priority of work to achieve the best possible defence in the time available.

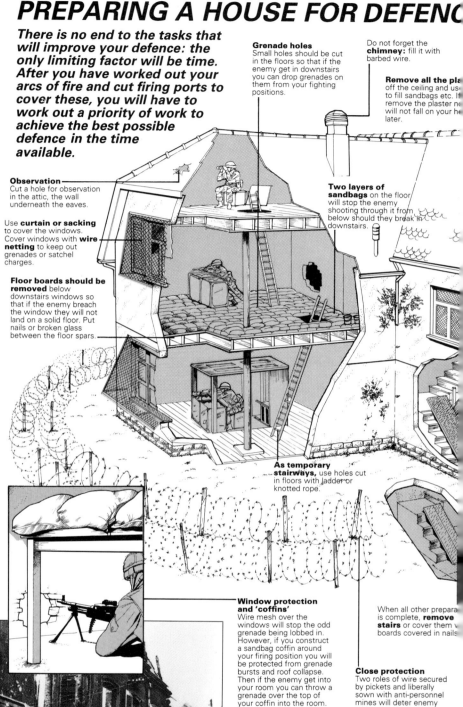

Grenade holes
Small holes should be cut in the floors so that if the enemy get in downstairs you can drop grenades on them from your fighting positions.

Do not forget the **chimney:** fill it with barbed wire.

Remove all the pla off the ceiling and use to fill sandbags etc. If remove the plaster ne will not fall on your he later.

Observation
Cut a hole for observation in the attic, the wall underneath the eaves.

Two layers of sandbags on the floor will stop the enemy shooting through it from below should they break in downstairs.

Use **curtain or sacking** to cover the windows. Cover windows with **wire netting** to keep out grenades or satchel charges.

Floor boards should be removed below downstairs windows so that if the enemy breach the window they will not land on a solid floor. Put nails or broken glass between the floor spars.

As temporary stairways, use holes cut in floors with ladder or knotted rope.

Window protection and 'coffins'
Wire mesh over the windows will stop the odd grenade being lobbed in. However, if you construct a sandbag coffin around your firing position you will be protected from grenade bursts and roof collapse. Then if the enemy get into your room you can throw a grenade over the top of your coffin into the room.

When all other prepara is complete, **remove stairs** or cover them boards covered in nails

Close protection
Two roles of wire secured by pickets and liberally sown with anti-personnel mines will deter enemy with mouseholing charges.

Public services
Gas is a real hazard, so turn it off outside the house: the same goes for the electricity. If the enemy gets in, having to fight in the dark gives you the advantage: you know the layout of the house, he does not.

Fighting in the dark
The rooms will be in total or semi darkness, so you can use neck wires and low wire entanglement in the rooms. This will slow the attacker up and give you time to get out of a lost room.

Traditional stone German housing is well suited to defence. They generally have cellars that will provide strongpoints and walls strong enough to stop small arms fire.

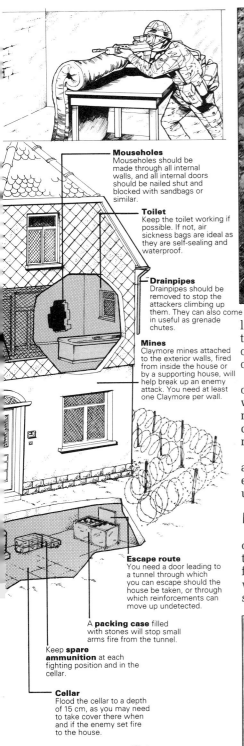

Mouseholes
Mouseholes should be made through all internal walls, and all internal doors should be nailed shut and blocked with sandbags or similar.

Toilet
Keep the toilet working if possible. If not, air sickness bags are ideal as they are self-sealing and waterproof.

Drainpipes
Drainpipes should be removed to stop the attackers climbing up them. They can also come in useful as grenade chutes.

Mines
Claymore mines attached to the exterior walls, fired from inside the house or by a supporting house, will help break up an enemy attack. You need at least one Claymore per wall.

Escape route
You need a door leading to a tunnel through which you can escape should the house be taken, or through which reinforcements can move up undetected.

A **packing case** filled with stones will stop small arms fire from the tunnel.

Keep **spare ammunition** at each fighting position and in the cellar.

Cellar
Flood the cellar to a depth of 15 cm, as you may need to take cover there when and if the enemy set fire to the house.

External doors should be blocked, locked and nailed shut. You can either sandbag them or fill cupboards with earth or bricks and put them in front of the doors.

Water
The water should be left on. Fill every container that will hold water and distribute them evenly between the rooms. Fill the baths and divert drain pipes to pipe rainwater into the house for collection.

Barricades should be liberally sowed with anti-personnel and anti-tank mines, and you should site anti-tank weapons to engage any armour attempting to clear it for the infantry.

All approaches to your house and likely forming-up points should be wired, mined and covered by fire. This type, the low-wire entanglement, is particularly effective as it is easy to conceal in long grass.

layers of it, perhaps up to head height, the infantryman is caught. He has no option but to find another way to his objective.

Only armoured vehicles are capable of penetrating wire easily, and they will be disabled by the anti-tank mines laid on the far side, where mine detectors can't get at them to mark and remove them.

Taken together, wire and mines are a very cheap way to hold up the enemy advance, but it takes time to set up a barrier as good as this.

Wiring a house

Wire can be used inside buildings on its own, too. Anything you can do to slow up the enemy will act in your favour. Use concertina wire in hallways and staircases. Fill up the whole space if you can. If you can't anchor it

into the floor, walls and ceiling, then wedge in wooden beams to stop incoming forces pushing it before them with doors or other makeshift shields.

Don't forget roof tops. They need to be defended against heli-borne troops as well as foot soldiers. On flat roofs you should use poles with the wire, to prevent helicopters from getting too close.

String concertina wire round the edges of the roofs, too, to stop roof-to-roof movement and make it impossible to rappel down off the roof into the upper storey windows.

Concertina wire makes a good win-

Lessons learned in street fighting in Germany towards the end of World War II provide the basis for current tactical doctrine. The Soviets have not forgotten these hard-learned lessons, as their FIBUA training and development of a variety of flame weapons clearly demonstrates.

dow obstacle. It allows the defenders to fire through it easily, but stops enemy troops from getting in. If it's thick enough, it may catch and hold grenades, so it should always be used loosely coiled, and backed up with wire mesh.

Properly anchored, barbed wire makes an impenetrable obstacle in underground tunnels and culverts. Reinforce it with booby traps and mines.

Tank traps

Effective as it is, wire on its own isn't enough to stop vehicles. Only three obstacles will stop a tank: a purpose-built anti-tank barricade such as the steel 'hedgehog' – which consists of three four-to-six foot steel girders welded and bolted together into three-dimensional crosses, and enough of them to fill up an entire street; a pile of rubble and rubble-filled vehicles so heavy that the tank can't push its way through it; or a crater that fills the whole width of the road.

Even then you'll need to lace the obstacles with anti-tank and anti-personnel mines and cover it with fire. The idea isn't necessarily to bar the way permanently, but to stop the tank long enough to direct killing fire from the 66mm LAW or the heavier TOW missiles on to it.

One way to close a road is to lay concertina wire at a junction, and then blow the houses on either side down on top of it. Mines and booby traps should be sown in the rubble to make the job of clearing even more difficult.

Another method is to fill a number of vehicles with rubble and earth, drive them into the road junction and then tip them over.

If there are no heavy vehicles available, take four cars and position them into a square. Turn them inwards on to their sides and fill the space in the centre with earth and rubble. If you

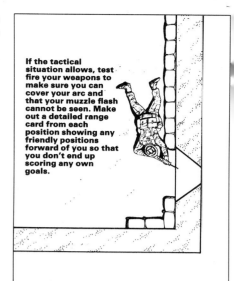

If the tactical situation allows, test fire your weapons to make sure you can cover your arc and that your muzzle flash cannot be seen. Make out a detailed range card from each position showing any friendly positions forward of you so that you don't end up scoring any own goals.

Loophole construction. Sandbagging will protect you from masonry chips and sustained machine-gun fire. To provide adequate protection, the sandbags must be at least two rows thick and damped down with water to reduce dust and fire hazard. V-shaped construction gives a better arc of fire while reducing your vulnerability to return fire.

can pour concrete in and around them, even better.

Mines and boobytraps

Mines can be anything from a few ounces of plastic explosive stuck with nails or other metal scraps, to factory-made objects capable of taking the track off a 60-ton tank. They can be the size of a coin, or as large as a dust-bin lid. Plastic mines need have no metal parts, so aren't vulnerable to discovery by metal detectors.

Mines can be employed equally effectively both where you can cover them with fire, and in locations that you can't oversee.

Because they are triggered by movement, mines can be as dangerous to people on your own side as to the enemy. Never set mines and booby

LOOPHOLE FIRE POSITIONS

First, use efficient recce to decide which arcs you have to cover with fire and how to achieve interlocking and overlapping arcs of fire. Then tell the troops exactly where to cut their loopholes. You must also consider

camouflage; loopholes cut like those below will draw fire. The aim is to see without being seen so that you can kill without being killed. In defence you have the advantage as you are not required to move, and there is plenty of

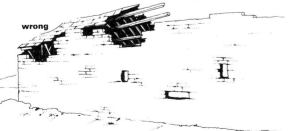

Cut your loopholes to cover your arcs. Remember, in FIBUA this is much more difficult and your arcs will be restricted; you may need to cut several for each soldier and block the spares until they are needed. Camouflage is all-important; this is the wrong way to do it.

sustained fire machine-gun can through a loophol like a shellhole. It must be in darkne so cover must be erected on the oth side to cut out the light

How you camouflage your fire position is limited only by your imagination. You could cut a hole in a door and lean it up against the wall covering the loophole, or disguise the loophole as a shell hole.

traps without noting their location and type on a sketch plan.

The trigger, too, is important. It may be a trip-wire, a pressure switch or a pressure release switch, or some kind of remote control mechanism. Make sure that the type of trigger used with every mine is marked down on the mine plan.

When a building or a piece of ground is mined, it should have sign posts to say so. The sign alone will probably be enough to weaken the enemy's morale and make him move more carefully and slowly, giving you the opportunity to bring him under fire.

You can use your imagination as to when and where these signs are placed. As long as they give the right information to your own troops, the enemy can be left to think what he pleases. Signs are cheaper than mines, after all!

For this reason, you must always be aware of where your mines have been laid. This can make for difficulties when one unit hands over to another, and all units must have one man, plus a back-up, whose job it is to be responsible for mine intelligence.

Slow the man down

Don't place mines and boobytraps in any set pattern. Of course, you'll put them in obvious places like the treads of a staircase, on window sills and in doorways, but always vary the actual site so that enemy troops have to stop and find them. Slowing them up so that you can engage them is almost as valuable as the mines killing them outright.

Lay the devices in depth. If he finds one, the enemy infantryman may relax and get hit by the next one before he's had a chance to concentrate again. The US Army's M14 anti-personnel mine is ideal for this purpose. It's small – the size of a large coin – so it's easy to hide, and because it's made entirely of plastic, it is very difficult to detect. Despite its size, it is capable of causing a very nasty wound.

The much larger M16 anti-personnel mine is ideal for covering larger areas such as rooftops, yards and cellars. It's best to trigger it from a location thirty or more yards away, with a wire or rope attached to its release pin. The advancing enemy troops may well see the actuating wire, but by that time they won't be in a position to do anything about it.

Plastic explosives

Claymore mines rely on their explosion alone for effect. You can pack shrapnel around them to turn them into anti-personnel mines, or use them to demolish walls. You can also take out the one and a half pounds of plastic explosive that they contain to make smaller boobytraps.

This plastic explosive is quite safe to handle. You can drop it, hit it with a hammer or even use it as fuel on the fire if things get really rough. It requires a detonator to set it off. Because of its Plasticine-like qualities, it's ideal for boobytraps.

The heavier M15, M19 and M21 anti-tank mines can be used with or without wire. If they're used on their own, choose a place where, once incapacitated, a tank will be difficult to move.

Make the enemy fight for every inch, and then, having done the damage, withdraw to your next prepared location. Here, on exercise, the 'enemy' make a break for it as the assaulting section moves in.

Even though tank recovery units will probably be in close support, you may delay the advance of an armoured column for quite some time. If you can overlook the ambush site with anti-tank rockets, so much the better.

By blocking all but one or two routes with tank-proof obstacles, and sowing the roads left clear with anti-tank mines, even a superior enemy force can be very seriously delayed.

Your positions on the edge of the town have forced the enemy to deploy to clear it. Having inflicted heavy losses you withdraw to your main defensive area of mutually supporting bunkers and strongpoints. It is time to stand and fight: if you lose a building that threatens your defence, it must be retaken. Your counter-attack has the advantage that you know the ground and have had time to plan a counter move for each building. Demolition charges can be concealed in the building and command-detonated should they fall to the enemy.

good cover in a town: make sure you do not give away your position through stupidity.

right

loophole covered by and in shadow of the ladder; if you use this, make sure the ladder is unclimbable

loophole hidden by a bundle of brushwood

loophole behind existing bush, or bush planted artificially

The best camouflage is something you can see through and shoot through while you stay hidden in shadow. Bushes or piles of firewood are ideal.

Combat Report
Borneo:
Battle against Indonesian Incursion

Alexander Ward, serving as second-in-command of the 1st Battalion Argyll and Sutherland Highlanders, tells of an incident during the Borneo campaign in the 1960s.

The armoured car in front of us laboured slowly up the slippery dirt road. Above the engine noise we could hear exploding artillery shells and the sharper detonations of mortar bombs. Overhead at intervals came the howl of the Royal Air Force Javelin fighter bombers, and from time to time the clatter of helicopter rotors.

Operation 'Mixed Bag'

Right beside the road, a Gurkha company from our brigade was unloading an air-drop they had just received. The small, tough-looking men seemed tired. Their jungle green uniforms were black with sweat and torn. One NCO had a blood-spattered field dressing on his arm. They had been in action for several days. When they saw us they paused and waved. They looked exactly what they were – superb, professional infantry soldiers. My driver looked at them and said, "Thank Christ they're on our side, sir!" I had to agree.

This was Operation 'Mixed Bag', the last battle of the Borneo campaign in the war that never was – it was euphemistically called a 'confrontation'. The conflict started after the state of Malaysia was formed in 1962, incorporating Malaya, Singapore, North Borneo, Brunei and Sarawak, and lasted until 1966.

President Sukarno of Indonesia had long wanted to be head of a Far East empire that would include some or even all of these countries, and so he started this undeclared

Borneo, 1966. Supplies drifting down by parachute to a company position of the Argyll and Sutherland Highlanders. The border with Indonesia was dotted with fortified British positions.

war. He trained Borneo Chinese in communist guerrilla tactics and sent them into North Borneo, supported by Indonesian regular troops. The latter were frequently RPKAD – para/commandos, good soldiers by any standards.

However, the people of North Borneo were content with British and then Malaysian rule. They hated the Indonesians, so Sukarno's men had little success. By 1966 the British and Malaysian forces had gained the upper hand but then, early in the year, the strong force of RPKAD and guerrillas crossed the border and a savage struggle began.

The battle started when local Dyak tribesmen spotted the enemy incursion and sent border scouts to report it. Our HQ was about 12 miles from the Indonesian border, and our rifle companies were in fortified bases almost on the border itself. The enemy came right into our area, and fighting broke out immediately.

Our commanding officer decided to move a small tactical headquarters from our base at Serian to our company forward base at Tebedu, 12 miles away on the border, which left me in charge of main HQ. We checked our defences in case of sudden attack, but sleep was difficult that night because of the constant drone of aircraft as RAF Shackletons dropped flares over the infiltrators' locations.

We sent for ammunition

The battle was disconcerting at this stage because our artillery, located on the Indonesian border, frequently swung round and fired back towards us! It was strange to hear the shells exploding only a couple of miles from our headquarters. An old soldier said the only time he had experienced that before was in the Western Desert campaign during the Second World War.

After several days' fighting we had to send ammunition, food and other necessities to our

forward base at Tebedu. Brigade headquarters had directed that any convoy travelling through the battle area must be escorted by armoured personnel. I volunteered to command this convoy.

The guns grew louder

The quartermaster and his staff spent hours checking items and loading the convoy. The armoured cars turned up as scheduled, and we set off as the jungle gently steamed in the morning sun. Apart from combat noise there were no disturbances, and the half-expected enemy ambush did not materialise. We moved on, past the Gurkha company, to within a mile of the Indonesian border. The noise of the artillery guns grew louder, and it transpired that our gunners were firing with medium artillery and howitzers.

We arrived at Tebedu, where you had to shout to make yourself heard. Added to the noise of guns were mortars and helicopters. Having been warned of our arrival, there was a reception party waiting, led by a young officer. The Jocks were stripped to the waist and looked fit and hard. They hurriedly began unloading the stores, and were soon sticky with sweat. The din of battle continued around us while two dead guerrillas were brought in by helicopter for identification. Like all dead men, they looked small, their green uniforms torn and bloodstained, and each man had several gaping wounds. On their shoulders was an insignia showing a flower, which struck me as incongruous.

The offloading complete, I had a few words with my colonel and delivered some mail. It was important that we returned to our base as soon as possible. Just as we were about to roll, a young officer waved and indicated that he had a message for me. "Sir," he said, "the Colonel's not at all pleased with you – someone forgot to load the whisky!"

There was no hi-tech solution to the Indonesian problem. It was an infantryman's war of endless patrol actions, since the enemy had to be met and defeated in the jungle.

Combat Skills

DEFENDING A VILLAGE

The perimeter force battle is a nasty game of cat and mouse. Fortunately you have the advantage of knowing the ground (or what is left of it) after the preparatory bombardment.

As part of NATO's forces defending Western Europe you're much more likely to find yourself defending a town than trying to dislodge enemy forces who have holed up in a built-up area. NATO strategy is to take advantage of Germany's widespread urban areas, and make them impassable to an attacker. As a defender, you'll easily outclass the enemy in local knowledge, and you can choose the best available defensive positions, and plan and prepare them in good time.

Set your defences of a town properly, distribute your men correctly and construct your strongpoints thoroughly, and you'll not only survive but blunt, stop and finally destroy the enemy's onslaught. This section of the Combat Skills course describes the British Army's approach to defending a built-up area.

You should divide your available forces into four main categories: the **Perimeter Force**, the **Disruption Force**, the main **Defensive Force** and the **Reserve**.

The Perimeter Force

This consists of a number of separate Reconnaissance Forces, whose job is to set up posts on the perimeter of the built-up area to cover the most likely approaches. Specifically, their tasks will be to give warning of the approach of the enemy, to engage and if possible to destroy enemy reconnaissance and leading elements and, finally, to force the enemy to deploy and mount a deliberate attack in order to break into the town.

If you are a member of the Perimeter Force, you will operate in small groups and will be expected to operate and fight in these groups until your

The key to survival after you have destroyed the enemy recce and forced him to deploy is knowing when to beat a hasty and, preferably, out-of-contact retreat to the main defensive position.

Combat Skills

Your perimeter force should prevent enemy recce and force the enemy to deploy to clear the town. These forces should be withdrawn as the battle proceeds and the line of least resistance should lead the enemy onto your killing ground, usually the main street and square.

Timed charges
Timed charges can be left in undefended houses to demolish them after they have been occupied by the attackers

Internal defences
Use all the available furniture to improve the internal defence of your building. Large sofas will absorb grenade fragments, and wardrobes and cupboards packed with dirt or brick will stop small-arms fire.

Cover from fire and view
Houses blown across the street can be used to give covered approaches to more exposed positions. As a commander, make sure that no two houses are alike in the way they are defended, in case the enemy benefits by experience.

Protection
All floors in your building should ideally be double-sandbagged as this will allow you to move from one position to another during the battle, but you will probably not have the time or the sandbags to do a complete job. The best method of protection is to build a sandbag 'coffin' around your fire position.

Fire positions
Barricades formed from demolished housing can used to conceal fighting positions, machine-guns snipers.

Counter-attack
If a strongpoint is taken you must immediately counter-attack so that the enemy does not get chance to reinforce or organise the defence of what he has just won.

Tunnelling
The sewers are an ideal communication system, but try to duplicate your communication routes as the enemy may decide to flood the sewers.

position becomes untenable. This task calls for strong nerves and great professionalism. When you have done your job you should make your way back to the main defended localities.

The Disruption Force

The job of the Disruption Force is to cover the ground between the Perimeter Force and the main defended localities in the heart of the town. If

DEFENDING A VILLAGE

Left: Low-wire entanglements liberally sown with anti-personnel mines will slow the enemy down and inflict casualties. The mouse hole looks tempting, but the white tape indicates a booby trap which will be armed when the defenders withdraw.

Preparatory demolition
To prevent the enemy taking up fire positions in housing that overlooks your position, blow the walls facing your position out so that you can shoot directly into the rooms.

Undefended housing
Buy yourself time by barricading all the entrances to undefended houses.

Clearing your fields of fire
Once you have decided which house you are going to use, demolish any external building that could be used as cover such as outside toilets and garages, once all useful stores have been removed. Friendly tanks and APCs can be used for this.

Booby trapping
All unoccupied houses should be mined and booby-trapped. Mk 7 anti-tank mines command-detonated from your strongpoint are very effective.

The anti-armour plan
All the main tank approaches to your position should be mined and covered by anti-tank weapons. Sight your positions to take advantage of shooting at the thin underside armour of a tank as it lumbers over a rubble barricade, and try to catch tanks in enfilade fire as they drive down the main street by shooting down the side-streets.

you are part of the Disruption Force this is your opportunity to use your imagination.

Your aim must be to delay, confuse and disrupt the enemy. You can do this with rubble, mines, overturned houses, booby-traps, snipers and tank-hunting patrols. You must cause the maximum casualties and delay the enemy, but at the same time lure him into the main defended localities where your main defensive force can trap and destroy him. You can do this by leaving the main routes, through the city leading to the defended localities, relatively unobstructed.

CONSTRUCTING ROADBLOCKS

The only roads that should be left open are those that channel the enemy onto your killing ground. All other routes should be blocked either by blowing buildings across them or by constructing roadblocks as shown.
1 The log crib below should be filled with rubble and the logs should be at least 20 cm in diameter. Aim to cover a barricade with fire from in front and behind so that the enemy cannot use it as cover.
2 The vehicle crib should have the cars chained together with the wheels removed.
3 When using buses or HGVs as roadblocks, the vehicles should face the enemy as shown. All barricades should be mined.

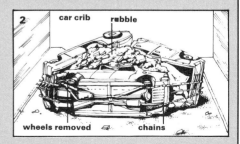

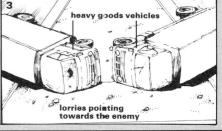

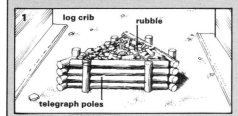

IMPROVISED ANTI-TANK DEVICES

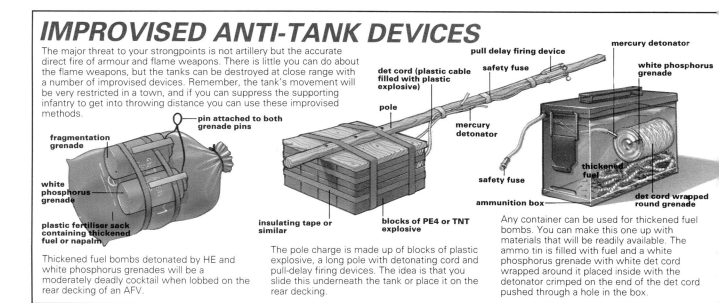

The major threat to your strongpoints is not artillery but the accurate direct fire of armour and flame weapons. There is little you can do about the flame weapons, but the tanks can be destroyed at close range with a number of improvised devices. Remember, the tank's movement will be very restricted in a town, and if you can suppress the supporting infantry to get into throwing distance you can use these improvised methods.

pin attached to both grenade pins

fragmentation grenade

white phosphorus grenade

plastic fertiliser sack containing thickened fuel or napalm

det cord (plastic cable filled with plastic explosive)

pole

pull delay firing device

safety fuse

mercury detonator

safety fuse

blocks of PE4 or TNT explosive

insulating tape or similar

mercury detonator

white phosphorus grenade

thickened fuel

ammunition box

det cord wrapped round grenade

Thickened fuel bombs detonated by HE and white phosphorus grenades will be a moderately deadly cocktail when lobbed on the rear decking of an AFV.

The pole charge is made up of blocks of plastic explosive, a long pole with detonating cord and pull-delay firing devices. The idea is that you slide this underneath the tank or place it on the rear decking.

Any container can be used for thickened fuel bombs. You can make this one up with materials that will be readily available. The ammo tin is filled with fuel and a white phosphorus grenade with white det cord wrapped around it placed inside with the detonator crimped on the end of the det cord pushed through a hole in the box.

The Main Defensive Force

Site the Main Defensive Force in strong positions in the heart of the town, with tank support if possible. This is where you hold and defeat the enemy. This is where you create your strongpoints and this is where you stay. If you have done your job properly you will be virtually impossible to budge.

There will be limited time available for reloading mags in the course of the defensive battle, and you will be using massive amounts of ammunition. Make sure you have an adequate supply of magazines.

The Reserves

If the enemy does manage to penetrate the main defended localities in some places, then you must commit your Reserves to seal off and destroy any penetration that has not been stopped by the Disruption Force. If any of your strongpoints are overrun then, it is up to the Reserves to counter attack and restore the position.

Choosing a strongpoint

This, in outline, is how you should plan to defend an urban area and how you should organise your available forces. But much more important is how you should organise your own strongpoint and how you should fight from it.

First, you must choose the right building. If you select one that is too small, then a single hit on the building from enemy artillery or a tank could well kill you and everyone in the building with you. On the other hand, if you choose too large a building, you may have to spread your defenders so thinly that you will be unable to cover all the approaches or provide an adequate concentration of fire to prevent the enemy storming the building. The selection of the right building to make into a strongpoint is probably your most difficult decision.

Structures and strength

When you have found a building that's the right size you must then make sure that it's of the most suitable construction. Avoid timber-framed buildings with a daub or brick infill. Old farmhouses and village houses are often of this type. They are inflammable and easily reduced to rubble,

particularly by a tank's main armament. Also avoid the typical modern bungalow or small two-storey house, which is often built from light materials such as plywood and light brick. Parts of these houses do not provide protection against even small arms fire.

High rise buildings, the basic framework of which is made from steel or reinforced concrete, infilled with reinforced concrete and large areas of glass, are not particularly suitable for defence either. Although you will find that they are excellent for observation purposes, there is a danger of progressive collapse if the building is damaged on the lower floors.

There is no doubt that the more traditional masonry house, with strong walls made of brick or stone, and probably three or four floors high, is much more suitable for defence. This type of house is usually pre-1940, has smaller windows, is much less flammable and has – certainly in Europe – good solid cellars. Its more modern version, built of brick or concrete block, with a pitched roof and concrete ground and upper floors is also very suitable for defence.

Look around you

The surroundings of a house should also affect your choice. Although it is important that you have good fields of fire from the house, it should ideally be neither isolated nor overlooked. Covered approaches to and from the building should be available, or you will not be able to receive reinforcements or supplies. Ideally, there should also be room for trenches in the garden so that you can prevent the enemy creeping up on the house.

Once you have chosen your strongpoint's house or houses you must put them in a state of defence. First of all there is much that you can do outside the strongpoint. You can block certain streets with rubble, or overturned vehicles, or both. You can erect wire obstacles and other types of barricade. You can lay mines and construct booby-traps around the houses themselves, to stop the enemy getting close enough to place pole charges against the building. You can also clear fields of fire so that you can engage the enemy early and effectively.

Strengthen your strongpoint

First, you can increase the protection provided by walls by placing sandbags against them. Earth-filled cupboards, chests of drawers, or even mattresses are very effective. Barricade all entrances except those you need to get in or out of the house – but you should be able to block even these at short notice.

Staircases and passages should also be blocked. You should move around inside the building through holes in the ceilings, which you should have specially prepared. You can come and go through these by ladders, ropes or even piled-up furniture.

Remember that all this preparation has probably put extra pressure on floors and ceilings, particularly cellars and ground-floor rooms. You should prepare for the shock of explosions by shoring up ceilings with strong timbers. Rest them on a solid base and wedge them into the solid parts of the ceiling. Finally, you should have plenty of water handy in each room, in basins, buckets and baths, ready for use in the event of fire. Gas and electricity should be turned off at the mains.

Placing men and weapons

When you have prepared the building, you should next site your defenders and their weapons. You should generally site automatic weapons near ground level. This is because a machine gun covers a long beaten zone if the rounds are travelling parallel to the ground. Its potential coverage must be greater then than if the gun is sited firing downwards.

Snipers, on the other hand, are engaging lone targets and are better sited higher up where they can see further. Throw hand grenades from first-floor level or higher. You should site hand-held anti-tank weapons in upper storeys, so that they fire down-

wards onto the relatively unprotected tops of armoured vehicles. However, remember that hand-held anti-tank weapons have a large back blast.

The firing position

If you are firing through a window with a rifle, stay as far back from it as possible so that you are not seen from the outside – but not so far that you cannot cover your arc. Even better, construct loopholes in unexpected places such as underneath a window sill or through the tiles in a roof, and fire through those. Your loopholes can be simple rectangular slits knocked through the brickwork, which will give you a wide arc of fire.

However, if you are covering a specific point, try to construct your loophole so that the aperture on the outside of the building is small, with a wider section on the inside so that it is V- or cone-shaped. To avoid splinters, surround your firing position with as many sandbags as possible. When your loophole is not in use, place something bullet-proof over the aperture to avoid the enemy firing or seeing through it.

You should, of course, remove all the glass from the windows and, if you have the stores and the time, replace it with anti-grenade wire netting. If you are using a window to fire through, ordinary net curtains are a simple and

German infantry equipped with 'Panzerfaust', a very primitive but effective RPG, enter a house. The German countermeasure when a room they were defending was successfully breached by the attackers was to vacate and clear out the new tenants by firing a Panzerfaust through a hole in the wall from the next room.

The enemy has no shortage of armour: if his tanks are allowed to move freely your strongpoint will not last long. Every effort must be made to isolate the infantry from his tanks and destroy as many tanks as possible during the perimeter battle to discourage further use of armour in the town.

effective way of preventing the enemy seeing into the house.

Tanks, artillery and mortars can play an effective role in an urban area, but remember that the more it is reduced to rubble the less vehicles can move. In the end it is you, the infantryman, who will have to emerge from the cellars when a bombardment is over and engage the enemy. Fighting in a built-up area is an unpleasant way of doing battle with the enemy, but it is an effective and realistic way for a numerically smaller force to stop and defeat a larger and stronger enemy.

Combat Report
Laos:
Dieter Dengler's Rescue

US Navy flier Dieter Dengler was shot down over Laos in February 1966. He was captured by the communist Pathet Lao, escaped, and was captured again. For five months, he and a handful of American and Thai prisoners were tortured, starved, denied medical treatment, and marched at gunpoint through the jungle. Then he escaped.

Dengler and his fellow prisoners overwhelmed their captors, but the others were too weak to flee with him. They either died or were recaptured. Half-crazed with malaria, covered with leeches, forty pounds below his usual weight, Dengler thrashed onwards in thick fog, through ice-cold mist, driven by a compulsion to survive.

But his escape seemed futile: there was nowhere to go. He was 300 miles from the nearest city, and lost in rain forests where visibility is restricted to a couple of metres. Guided only by the sound of a nearby river, all he could do was to keep walking.

I met Dengler when I was sent to Pleiku in 1966, to command the US Air Force's first Air Commando Squadron, known as Hobo, flying prop-driven A-1 Skyraiders. I was carrying out combat missions in South Vietnam and Laos.

On the morning of 20 July 1966, I was scheduled for a Skyraider armed reconnaissance mission. I was delayed because of a radio failure on my plane. Later that morning, I was ready to go again when my wingman developed mechanical problems. Another delay.

We were a stubborn lot, I guess, but I've often thought how easy it would have been not to go up that July day. The weather was terrible: it was overcast, making any kind of flying difficult. With two postponements already, it would have been easy to say, "to hell with it." But for some reason, although it was

Dieter Dengler (right) and I photographed in 1967, 18 months after we met in the Laotian jungle.

too late for my original mission, I decided to go anyway.

By early afternoon, trying to get in one mission beneath 500 ft overcast, I was flying over a rock outcrop in a stream bed in Laos. I came up the stream at low level, made a sharp turn, and spotted what looked like a fisherman waving at me with a net. I kept going, but something nagged at me. Hadn't that "fisherman" darted out of the jungle just when I was above him? "Let's go back there," I radioed my wingman.

"I think I can see an SOS"

"I don't get it," I said out loud. That man could easily see my Skyraider was fully armed with CBUs (cluster bomb units), rockets and 20-mm cannon. A communist guerrilla, or even an innocent peasant, would be likely to run for cover. But this small, thin figure was still waving frantically at me.

"Colonel," my wingman broke in, "I think I see an SOS written on that rock."

SOS was indeed written, very awkwardly, on the rock. I knew that the gomers sometimes set up "flak traps" to bait American pilots into flying low, but something about that figure on the riverbank struck a chord with me. I radioed a C-130 airborne command post nearby to ask if any "friendlies" had been shot down. The answer was a firm No.

I climbed, cut the power and circled over the river, remaining just beneath the ceiling of grey soup. I attempted to call an O-1 Bird Dog spotter plane in the area, but with the 500 ft ceiling the spotter couldn't reach us. Meanwhile, two more Skyraiders from Pleiku joined us on our wing, but I sensed a mood of resistance: having been suckered by the enemy so often, they didn't like my preoccupation with that lone figure.

I raised Saigon on the radio and was firmly told to give up. However, when they heard I was a lieutenant colonel and a squadron commander they became less firm. Reluctantly, Saigon authorised a Jolly Green helicopter to attempt a pick-up. There was some speculation that the man might be an enemy defector with valuable information.

I was low on fuel, but I wanted to see this through to the end. Other "friendly" aircraft in the area were being fired on, and we didn't know if the enemy had hidden guns aimed at us. With an understandably reluctant crew, the HH-3E helicopter came up the river, got into

An HH-3E helicopter used to rescue downed airmen.

position above the guy, and lowered a penetrator.

As I looked down, I half expected to hear the crunch of enemy shells ripping into me at any moment. My life flashed before my eyes. Well, not my life exactly, but certainly my career in the Air Force. "That guy is going to turn out to be a gomer," I told myself. "As soon as they reel him in, he's going to pull out a grenade and die for Ho Chi Minh. We'll lose a chopper and my ass will go from lieutenant colonel to airman, third class."

"Who is this guy?"

I was in radio contact with the chopper pilot, but we were not communicating very effectively. Finally I could wait no longer. I asked, "Who is the guy?"

"Beats the hell out of us. He looks half dead."

"Is he ours or theirs?"

There was a pause. There must have been some shuffling going on as the helicopter jerked up and started away. I think the crew were holding the guy down.

"This guy is a mess!" someone exclaimed.

Finally: "Sir, this guy claims to be a Navy lieutenant who was shot down in Laos six months ago."

My Skyraider flight and the HH-3E diverted to Da Nang. Later I learned that we had rescued Navy pilot Dieter Dengler. If I'd stuck to my original flying schedule that day, or succumbed to temptation when delay could have led to cancellation, Dengler would never have been saved. Though we didn't meet until it was over, we have since become good friends.

This is a Douglas A-1 Skyraider of the sort I was flying when I spotted Dieter Dengler waving frantically in the jungle.

DEFENCE AGAINST AIR ATTACK

In any conflict in north-west Europe, NATO forces would be operating under conditions of enemy air superiority and so you, as a fighting infantryman on foot or in a vehicle, would be particularly vulnerable to air attack. You can expect attack from Soviet helicopter-borne forces, parachute troops, bomblets, rockets or chemical weapons, and will be under constant threat during daylight and in fair weather conditions.

To counter this threat, specialist low-altitude air defence weapons such as Rapier and Blowpipe would probably be deployed in your battle-group area, and they should provide some protection. However, the danger is so strong that you yourself will have to take a number of additional measures.

Passive measures

1 Concealment The enemy cannot attack you from the air if he cannot see you, so you must conceal yourself effectively. This means camouflaging trenches, vehicles, equipment and stores with camouflage netting. It means sensible and irregular siting of equipment using cover and shadow. Restrict your daylight movement and, if it is really necessary, maintain track plans. When aircraft are flying overhead, you must keep still and not look up.

2 Protection Having concealed yourself effectively, protect yourself by sitting yourself in areas that are difficult to attack from the air. A good example of this technique was the choice of San Carlos Water for an anchorage and landing beach during the 1982 Falklands conflict; the surrounding mountains made a straight run-in for attacking aircraft extremely difficult. You must also protect yourself by digging yourself in: a properly-dug slit trench can withstand all but a direct hit by rockets or bombs.

3 Warning However good your protection, it is no good unless you are in it, so you need a good warning system. This means a proper system of air sentries who can provide sufficient warning of air attack and allow you to take cover in your trench.

Above: Firing the Blowpipe missile: a guided SAM used by the British Army, which you visually guide towards the target aircraft using a thumb control. It was used successfully in the Falklands.

A shoulder-fired anti-aircraft missile can bring down the most powerful aircraft, as long as you manage to hit it. Here a target aircraft is successfully destroyed during tests. In battle, however, shooting down hostile aircraft is difficult and dangerous.

The US Army's Stinger missile is a 'fire and forget' weapon. An infra-red seeker in its nose enables the missile to home in on the heat emissions from a target aircraft. Since many air forces employ countermeasures such as dropping flares to confuse this sort of homing device, an ultra-violet detector will probably be fitted to the improved Stinger currently under development.

Combat Skills

4 Dispersion If, however, you are in the open advancing across a piece of open countryside, your best protection will be to ensure that at all times you are properly dispersed. Sections must keep well apart, and you in your section should keep a sensible distance from your battle partner.

Statistically speaking, if a bomb devastates 50 square metres, only two men are in danger if you're 25 metres apart, whereas four men are in danger if you're huddled up only 12 metres apart. Similarly, if you're in a vehicle convoy you should be divided into packets several miles apart; enemy aircraft cannot attack you all at once.

Active measures: small-arms fire

Active air defence measures by the infantry will cause casualties to enemy aircraft. Within the infantry platoon, this means engaging enemy aircraft and helicopters with small-arms fire. Ideally, fire at an aircraft should never be less than a single automatic weapon or a section of riflemen, and in either case it should be controlled, where possible, by an NCO.

The aim must be to put up a wall of small-arms fire so that any attacking aircraft must be hit by something: an individual rifleman firing at an aircraft will be ineffective. The most effective form of small-arms fire is an automatic weapon on a pintle mount, which allows the weapon to be elevated without having to lift it.

Since the introduction of the Light Support Weapon (LSW) into the rifle section, all GPMGs have been re-allocated so that as many tracked and wheeled vehicles throughout the British Army are now armed with a GPMG that is easily used in the AA role.

The Falklands War demonstrated the effectiveness of small-arms fire in

*Above: The **GPMG** can be an effective anti-aircraft system weapon, especially if enough of them are pointed in the same direction.*

*Below: The **GPMG** is more accurate in the **AA** role if you have time to fit it to a proper anti-aircraft mount, rather than simply firing it from the kneeling position.*

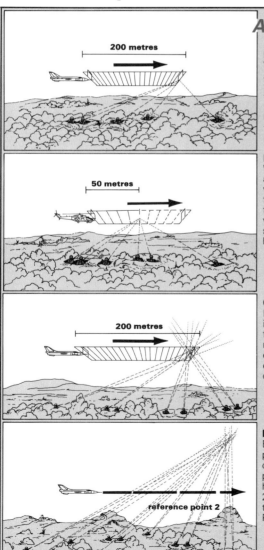

AIMING AT AIRCRAFT

High-performance aircraft
When firing a rifle, GPMG or LSW against a fast jet flying low across your front, aim about 200 metres (two football pitches) in front of it. With the SA80, don't try to use the optical sight because you will never acquire the target. Fire controlled bursts from the hip.

Low-performance aircraft
When shooting at a helicopter or other aircraft which flies much more slowly, you need to allow only 50 metres (half a football pitch) lead. But remember that friendly helicopters can appear above you unexpectedly, and you should only shoot if you can positively identify it as hostile.

Concentrated fire
Infantry weapons must be concentrated if they are to stand a chance of hitting a fast jet. If a whole platoon aims at roughly the same spot ahead of an enemy aircraft, you will hopefully put enough rounds in its path to score some damage.

Reference point
By shooting at a pre-arranged reference point it is easier for a platoon to place a concentrated fire pattern squarely in the path of the enemy aircraft. Here, a hill has been designated as reference point 2 and as soon as a target flies towards it the commander orders: 'Reference Point 2: Fire'.

[Diagram labels: 200 metres; 50 metres; 200 metres; reference point 2]

The best way to destroy aircraft is when they are on the ground: this Argentine Pucará was destroyed on its runway during the Falklands war. If the enemy are operating aircraft within the possible range of a fighting patrol, a successful raid can cause enormous damage.

modern warfare against fast jets. Several Argentine jets were shot down either by small-arms fire from soldiers entrenched in defensive positions, or from machine-guns strapped to the railings of ships. If enough rounds are fired continuously into a 'slice' of air space some must hit a vulnerable point such as a fuel tank, causing a catastrophic loss of fuel: many Argentine aircraft were lost during their return to base on the mainland due to loss of fuel caused by small-arms fire.

Clearly, there is a danger that infantrymen whose aircraft recognition is poor may fire at friendly aircraft. In an infantry platoon you will be told which of two aircraft engagement states prevail: 'Weapons Tight' means that aircraft must not be engaged unless you recognise them as positively hostile, as defined in the Rules of Engagement. This is the normal air defence state in a battlegroup area. 'Hold Fire' is an emergency order meaning that you must 'cease fire', or that 'you should not open fire'.

This is normally used in a battle group area to safeguard Army aviation that may be operating in your area for short periods: for instance, a squadron of TOW Lynx helicopters may be due in your area to take up fire positions to engage a major tank threat. As soon as they have left, 'Weapons Tight' will be reimposed.

The Rules of Engagement will vary according to the theatre you are operating in and, anyway, they will form part of your battalion Standard Operating Procedures (SOPs). They will usually include the following rules:

1 Helicopters and light aircraft

You should not fire unless the aircraft is recognised as hostile by an officer or NCO. This is because friendly light aircraft and helicopters are liable to fly anywhere without notice and may dive suddenly in order to take evasive action.

2 High performance aircraft

You should not fire unless the aircraft is seen to attack a position. Only the position attacked or those adjacent to it should retaliate.

3 Transport aircraft or transport helicopters

You should not fire unless aircraft are identified as hostile and are seen to be landing troops or dropping parachutists or stores.

These rules have been worked out as a result of bitter experience in a number of campaigns when friendly aircraft have been shot down by overzealous soldiers.

Aircraft have to slow down

Combat Skills

to identify and attack a ground target, and they normally need to make a number of passes to identify and attack effectively. This allows you more than one chance to engage them, and the pilot can hear the crack of bullets going past him and see tracer if you are using it. Small arms fire can:

1 Damage the aircraft so that it does not make it back to base or, if it does, ensure that it is grounded for several days for repair.

2 Upset the pilot's aim, causing him to miss the target, make another pass or even abandon the mission.

3 Force the enemy aircraft to climb to a height where other air defence systems can engage him.

4 Make enemy aircraft attacks less effective by forcing the pilots to fly faster.

The GPMG is the most effective infantry weapon for use against aircraft, though you can use the LSW or your SA80 to add to the volume of fire. The GPMG is pintle-mounted in all British Army armoured and many soft-skinned vehicles.

When you decide to engage an enemy aircraft with the GPMG you should, if the aircraft is coming straight at you, point the gun at its nose. If it is slow and crossing, point the gun well in front of its line of direction so that it flies into the path of the bullets. You must swing with the aircraft.

You should fire a 50-round belt whenever possible in one controlled burst, making corrections yourself by watching the tracer or by following the instructions of the gun controller – if there is one. Obviously, if you see your tracer pass behind a crossing air-craft you should make a bold swing forward to correct your aim.

You can also use your SA80 or LSW to fire at aircraft: you can do this with the aid of your sling from the standing or kneeling position. If you attempt to look through the single point ×2 magnification sight, you are unlikely to be able to acquire a fast-moving target, so the best technique is to fire controlled bursts from the hip, pointing the weapon in the general direction of the approaching aircraft. When firing from a trench you should lean against the back of it for support.

During peacetime, you will practise anti-aircraft small-arms firing by firing at a small radio-controlled fixed-wing aircraft called MATS(A), which is in effect a model aircraft. MATS(A) tend to survive for a long time because they are such a small target, but despite this they fly realistic aircraft attack patterns and provide valuable anti-air-craft engagement experience. They can also absorb several hits which can easily be repaired. Even if damage is sustained, a parachute is deployed and this allows the aircraft to be recovered and repaired.

You will face attack from aircraft on the modern battlefield. As an infantryman you can fight back, but it must be a team effort. Your section or your platoon must co-ordinate its fire to be effective. If you do this, you will eat away at the enemy's air strength and keep his aircraft off your back.

Pilots who have bailed out of disabled aircraft should not be fired at. Engaging parachuting pilots is a violation of the Geneva convention.

Above: If enemy paratroops land near you, aim about two man-heights below them to allow for their rate of descent.

Below: Now that the GPMGs in British sections are being replaced by LSWs, many more GPMGs are available to provide AA defence on Army vehicles.

In the British Army you practice anti-aircraft shooting against radio controlled aircraft called MATS(A) which presents you with a slow-moving but very tiny target.

Above: Wheeled transport must evade immediately if attacked by enemy aircraft. Each truck should turn away from the aircraft's direction of attack, disperse and seek cover.

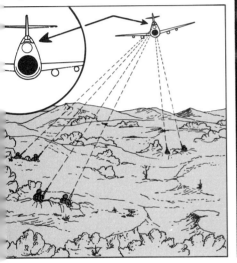

Above: If an aircraft is flying directly at you, aim just above its nose to produce a line of fire that it will fly into.

Above: Used by the US Army but now being replaced by Stinger, Redeye has difficulty in hitting aircraft that use flare dispensers.

Inset: Blowpipe is a command-guided point defence weapon: difficult to engage a crossing target with, but not vulnerable to flare dispensers.

Afghan guerrillas examine the wreckage of a Soviet Mi-24 'Hind' gunship which they shot down in the Panjsher valley. Some have been shot down by machine-gun fire from above after the guerrillas sited 12.7-mm guns on mountain-tops and shot up helicopters flying below them in the valleys.

HEALTH IN A HOT CLIMATE

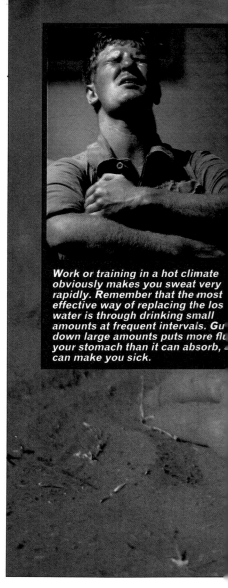

Work or training in a hot climate obviously makes you sweat very rapidly. Remember that the most effective way of replacing the los water is through drinking small amounts at frequent intervals. Gu down large amounts puts more flu your stomach than it can absorb, can make you sick.

A lot of military training is still carried out overseas. Years ago, troops went out by sea, and the long voyage would give them time to acclimatise to the tropical environment. Nowadays, flying out means that you can be deposited in a tropical country without any period of acclimatisation. Heat-related illnesses can be a danger even without exceptionally hot weather. Strenuous training when unfit in warm weather can cause it – and heat exhaustion can kill.

Body temperature

The body temperature must be maintained close to its norm of about 37°C to stay healthy. In addition to heat from the sun, and reflected heat from the ground and surrounding objects, any physical activity produces heat. To maintain the normal body temperature, this heat must be lost. This is done by sweating, which causes heat to be released from the body as it evaporates. In a climate where the temperature is over 30°C a man may lose 10-15 litres of sweat a day, even without exerting himself. This amount of water needs to be replaced.

In addition to the water loss, there will be salt lost in your sweat. If the body is not acclimatised, this loss can be serious and can result in heat cramps. Salt added to food should be sufficient to replace this, but it should not be added to water without medical advice. There is, however, a safe alternative which can be added to your water bottle. This is Dioralyte, a compound of the minerals and salts lost through sweating.

Prevention of heat illness

It is much easier to prevent heat illness than to treat it.

Acclimatisation

A period of acclimatisation helps the body to adjust to the heat: the main effect is to reduce the salt loss in the sweat to about half its previous levels. The blood vessels on the skin dilate, so increasing the amount of heat loss. This normally takes about three weeks.

Fluid intake

No-one can be trained to do without water; it's dangerous and will make you ill. Obviously, your liquid intake does not have to be restricted to pure water. Fruit juices and tea are just as good. Be careful with alcoholic drinks, since alcohol is a diuretic and causes you to pass more fluid as urine than you take in. It is possible to raise your body fluid levels before an arduous exercise by drinking more than normal (but not alcohol) in the 12 to 24 hours before the start of the exercise.

Shelter

Your shelter should also be light in colour to reflect the heat, and should allow air to circulate and provide shade.

Light-coloured clothing helps to reflect the heat. It should be loose-fitting to allow air to circulate, as in the issue jungle camouflage shirt which is designed to be worn outside your trousers, not tucked in. These American soldiers are wearing current issue desert uniform.

General health

Your general health is important. Personal hygiene is essential, and you must pay particular attention to your skin and feet. If you're overweight your body will be less able to respond effectively to heat: strenuous physical activity can cause heat illness even in this country for those who are unfit or unused to it.

Heat illnesses

There are a variety of heat illnesses, which will be dealt with in increasing order of severity.

Sunburn

Sunburn is a form of superficial burn that can be prevented. One day in the sun will not give you a tan, but it could give you serious burns. Wear clothes that cover as much of your skin as possible, and do not spend too much time in the sun: half an hour on the first day is more than enough.

Prickly heat

Some people are more susceptible than others: it is an irritable condition of the skin. Your skin needs to be kept very clean, but soap can make it worse, so rinse it off thoroughly after washing. Hair must also be regularly washed but well rinsed. Loose, clean clothing should be worn, including clean underclothes.

Heat cramps

Heat cramps are caused by a lack of salt in the body. They can happen in any part of your body and can be quite severe, but are easily prevented by ensuring that there is adequate salt in your diet. If they do occur, seek medical help.

Some soldiers stand a greater risk of falling victim to heat injury. Keep an eye on recruits doing their basic training and on anyone with a history of previous heat injury or a weight problem.

Heat exhaustion

This can happen when you're working hard in relatively high temperatures, and is more likely to happen if you're overweight or unfit: excessive sweating causes abnormal fluid and salt loss, leading to circulatory failure. This results in:

1 Headache, nausea and dizziness.
2 Pale, clammy skin.
3 Weak, rapid pulse progressing to hot, flushed, dry skin and full, bounding pulse.
4 Cramps.

The casualty will have the signs of shock plus heat cramps. The body temperature may be normal or slightly raised. If not treated, the casualty may become unconscious.

Treatment

Lie the casualty down in a cool place. Remove as much of their clothing as possible, and give them frequent small drinks of water to which salt has been added: half a teaspoon of salt or sodium bicarbonate to a litre. Get them to drink as much as you can and get medical help as soon as possible. In combat, if the casualty is unconscious, insert the rectal drip set to restore the fluid balance, since at least 60 per cent of water is absorbed by the colon.

Heat cramps and heat exhaustion are relatively straightforward problems, solved by administering water and salt. Heatstroke, however, is a medical emergency which can be fatal. Watch particularly for a collapsed casualty who stops sweating.

Heatstroke

Heatstroke is a very serious condition that if not recognised and treated quickly can result in severe brain damage and death. The heat-regulating mechanism of the body ceases to work and the temperature keeps on rising. The brain literally cooks. The signs of heat stroke include:
1 Disturbed behaviour.
2 Delirium, partial loss of consciousness and coma.
3 Tiredness, headache and irritability.
4 Nausea and vomiting.
5 Reduced or absence of sweating.
6 Strong, bounding pulse.
7 Hot, flushed and dry skin.

The casualty's temperature must be reduced by whatever means are possible. He should be moved into a cool dry place and have his clothing removed and then sponged down with tepid water, or if possible wrapped in a wet sheet. In both cases, fan the body to assist cooling. Give frequent small drinks of water. Get him proper medical help without any delay.

FIGHTING THE COLD

Working in a cold climate can cause major health problems. The physical effects of cold cause real difficulties, but in addition the loss of morale caused by the cold can in itself lead to further trouble. Problems with the cold are not confined to the Arctic or mountain regions. They also happen in relatively mild climates, especially when associated with wetness. Exposure causes a substantial number of casualties and even some deaths on exercises in the UK.

Dry cold

Dry cold is typical of Arctic regions and is characterised by very low temperatures and often biting winds. The temperature may be down to –30°C or even lower.

Wet cold

Wet cold occurs in more temperate regions where the ice and snow melts, and there may be rain. The temperature is rarely as cold as in Arctic areas for more than occasional short periods.

Dutch marines on exercise in Norway. Low temperatures low relative humid (dry cold) favours development of frostbite. Higher temperatures toget with moisture tend lead to trench foot. Wind chill accelera the loss of body he and aggravates bo conditions.

Cold illnesses

Hypothermia

Hypothermia simply means sub-normal body temperature. It is often called exposure when it happens outside and hypothermia when it affects old people indoors, but it's the same thing. There are a number of factors that may lead to hypothermia:

1 Lack of Food
Food provides the energy for the body to produce heat. To combat cold, the calorific value of the food needs to be increased. Lack of food will lower the ability to cope with cold.

2 Poor clothing
In cold weather, you need extra clothing. Multiple layers that trap air are the most effective way of retaining body heat. You lose a lot of heat through your head and feet, so make sure you have proper headgear and footwear.

3 Dirty clothing
Wet, damp and dirty clothing is a poor insulator and increases heat loss. Keep your clothes clean, and remove damp or wet clothing during rest periods and dry it out. This applies particularly to footwear: socks must be changed and boots allowed to dry as much as possible.

4 Alcohol
Alcohol causes the blood vessels in the skin to dilate, which increases heat loss. Alcohol may make you feel warmer, but in reality it has the opposite effect.

US Army cold weather gear, seen here worn in South Korea, recognises the need to protect the face. Remember not to touch metal with your bare hands, and avoid spilling petrol on your skin or clothing. A high standard of personal admin is essential if you want to avoid cold weather injury.

Treatment

The casualty should be warmed slowly. Change any wet clothes and place him in a warm environment in a bed or sleeping bag. It may be necessary for someone else to get in as well to provide gentle heat. Cover his head to reduce heat loss. Moderately hot, sweet drinks will provide energy and gradually raise the temperature. DO NOT GIVE ALCOHOL. Evacuate the casualty as soon as possible.

Snow blindness

This is a temporary blindness caused by direc and reflected light. Snow is a very good refle and will exacerbate the effects of the sun. Th eyes become sensitive to glare, blinking increases and the eyes begin to water and fe irritable. Sight begins to have a pinkish tinge, and eventually the vision is covered by what appears to be a red curtain. At the same time the pain increases, so it can be a very frightening condition. Fortunately, the eyes w recover, given time, if they are covered with pads and rested. It can be avoided altogether wearing proper sunglasses.

Sunburn

Just as the light effects of the sun on the eye are increased in snow, so are the tanning effects on exposed skin. You may need to us cream, especially on your lips.

Foster Grants may not make you look like Al Pacino, but they will stop you suffering from snow blindness. Caused by the glare from an ice field or snow field, it is perversely more likely to occur in hazy or cloudy conditions than when the sun is shining brightly. At such times it is easy to forget the power of the sun and neglect basic precautions.

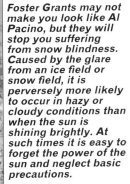

Frostbite

...ostbite is what happens when body tissues ...eeze, and it is your extremities that are most ...lnerable to attack. Unfortunately the onset of ...ostbite can often go unnoticed until it is too ...e. The freezing prevents body fluids reaching ...e affected tissues and they will eventually die. ...hen this happens, they will slowly turn black ...d drop off, but the damage is done long ...fore this stage is reached. In the early stages ...e affected parts are cold, firm, numb and ...arble white. It is essential to recognise ...ostbite at this stage to avoid lasting damage.

Treatment

...e body heat to warm the affected part, while ...casing the whole body in a sleeping bag. Hot ...nks may be given, and the casualty should ...en be evacuated.

...O NOT:
...Rub the injured part.
...Expose the injured part to fire or similar heat.
...Exercise the injured part.

...Frostbite can be prevented if the proper ...thing is worn, especially on the hands and ...et, which are the parts most at risk.

Immersion foot

Immersion foot, also known as trench foot, is caused by a lack of blood circulation and prolonged exposure to wet conditions. There are three stages:

1 The feet become white, numb and cold.
2 The feet become red, hot and painful.
3 The feet can become swollen, develop cellulitis (a form of inflammation) and eventually gangrene.

Prevention

You can take various measures:
1 Keep your circulation going by exercise.
2 Do not restrict your circulation with tight boots or with tight bindings round the bottom of trousers.
3 Keep your feet as dry as possible
4 Change socks daily and use powder on your feet.
5 Keep your feet clean.
  Properly cared-for feet should give little trouble.

Treatment

1 Remove boots and socks and warm and dry the casualty's feet, handling them gently. Do not rub or massage them or expose them to fire.
2 Elevate the feet.
3 Put the casualty into a sleeping bag.
4 Give hot drinks.
5 Give Paracetamol.
5 Evacuate the casualty as a stretcher case.

Vehicle crew sometimes have the advantage of a heater, but always have the disadvantage of sitting still in bitter cold weather. You just have to pile on the layers – women's tights are useful – and get on with it.

AVOIDABLE HEALTH HAZARDS

Personal hygiene and concern for your immediate camping or training environment are important. It is also advisable to avoid substances which actively increase the probability of ill health, and harm the body, such as alcohol, tobacco and drugs. All these substances are addictive, and once you've started it's very hard to stop. The degree of addiction can vary, but anyone can become hooked.

Smoking

For many years smoking has been known to be harmful: even the tobacco companies acknowledge this. The addictive element is the nicotine. The major harmful effects are caused by other substances such as tars and carbon monoxide that are produced by burning tobacco.

Smoking mainly attacks the lungs and heart. Lung cancer, heart attacks and bronchitis are all linked to smoking.

Lung cancer

The commonest form of lung cancer normally occurs only in smokers. This does not mean that all smokers will get lung cancer; the great majority will not. What it does mean is that non-smokers will almost certainly not suffer from lung cancer.

Heart disease

The largest single preventable cause of early death is coronary heart disease. Smokers have a very much higher chance of heart attacks, often leading to death, than do non-smokers: this is particularly so in men in their early 40s, and even young male smokers probably run a greater risk than non-smokers. Again, not every smoker will get a heart attack, and not every heart attack victim is a smoker. It is, however, absolutely clear that smokers run a very much higher risk of serious heart trouble than non-smokers. The sooner a smoker stops smoking, the better his chances; the longer he leaves it, the greater the risk of permanent damage.

How smoking damages your lungs: on the left is a cross-sectioned healthy lung; on the right, a lung removed from a smoker. The latter is choked with tar deposits and has a massive cancer in the middle, which has blocked the windpipe. The long-term effects of smoking are serious, and in the short term you are reducing your ability to manage sustained exercise.

Lung disease

Not surprisingly, smoking damages the lungs. The lungs have a very sensitive lining, designed to allow the exchange of oxygen from the air into the blood: it is not designed to cope with smoke and all its components.

The incidence of chronic bronchitis and long-term lung damage is very much higher in smokers. There are other possible causes, but these are becoming much less common. Bronchitis is fast becoming a smoker's disease.

Unfortunately, the effects of smoking are not immediately apparent. Young people can easily kid themselves everything is fine; they say that when they begin to suffer will be the time to give up. But by that time the damage will have been done, and of course the longer the addiction continues the harder it is to give up. You cannot guarantee good health, but you can give it a fighting chance by stopping or not starting smoking.

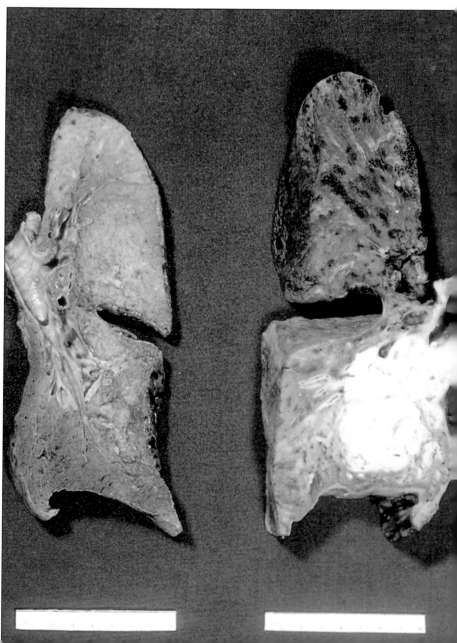

Alcohol

Alcohol has fewer addictive qualities than nicotine and, in moderation, has relatively few ill effects. It is, however, a poison. It has a depressant effect on the brain, but at first appears to be stimulating because the first thing it depresses are your inhibitions, making you more lively and talkative.

As the dose increases, so does the depressant effect. It is less easy to control personal behaviour, so fighting becomes more likely and the control of machinery is more difficult. One of the biggest problems is that it is almost impossible for an intoxicated person to realise and accept that their driving ability has been seriously impaired.

The poisonous effect of alcohol becomes more obvious the larger the amount taken. A blood level of about 400mg/100ml is often fatal in itself. The after-effects are proportional to the amount consumed. Hangovers are due to a variety of factors – a combination of the toxins acting on the brain, dehydration from the diuretic properties of alcohol, and a low blood sugar level. The liver is an organ which is especially sensitive to the effects of alcohol, because it is where the alcohol is broken down and detoxified. Long-term alcohol intake can lead to permanent liver damage, known as cirrhosis of the liver.

Drinking moderately is not normally a health risk, but there are circumstances when it should obviously be avoided. Any time you need to keep a clear head, such as walking or climbing in the mountains, your life and the lives of others could depend on your having absolute control, unclouded by alcohol.

Drugs

There are a wide variety of controlled drugs, ranging from the relatively innocuous cannabis to the potentially lethal heroin and cocaine. There are claims that cannabis is less harmful and addictive than tobacco, but there is no doubt that it clouds the judgement, which is particularly dangerous in a combat situation or training exercise when errors of judgement could be fatal. Once you start experimenting, it can be difficult to resist the temptation to move on and try harder and more dangerous drugs that are being pushed by the same dealers.

Heroin and cocaine are much more addictive than cannabis or alcohol. You can get hooked the first time you try it. Say no. Once you are hooked, it is extremely difficult to get off. Your health will rapidly be destroyed. In addition to the effects of the drug itself, injecting with dirty needles can give you infections, septicaemia, hepatitis and AIDS.

Some trials have been done, mainly in America, on drugs that have a stimulant effect. It was thought that such drugs might help soldiers to perform more effectively in battle, but the results were so unpredictable, with soldiers attacking their friends and so on, that these ideas have been totally abandoned.

Above: Aftermath of a US Military Police raid on a US Army base in Vietnam. With opium-tipped cigarettes cheaper than Marlboro, instant oblivion was an easy option.

Above: The poppy fields of Asia are big business and defy international attempts at destroying them. They trade on human weakness and gullibility. Drugs are not smart; they are a sure route to a degrading and disgusting end.

Right: Drug abuse in the American forces in Vietnam reached epidemic proportions in the early 1970s. Low morale led to dope and to worse morale in a vicious circle that destroyed the combat efficiency of whole units.

Air Defence with the Gepard

Since the 1960s NATO has lagged behind the Warsaw Pact in its front-line air defences. Although hand-held systems such as the British Javelin and United States Stinger are now issued in abundance, Gepard is still the only effective self-propelled air defence gun in the Western Alliance.

In the 1960s, the newly-reorganized West German army issued a requirement for a new self-propelled, all-weather anti-aircraft gun to replace the outdated M42 system. After extensive tests, a prototype, developed by Contraves AG of Zurich, Switzerland, was accepted, and a firm order for 475 vehicles (420 for West Germany and 55 for Belgium) was placed. The Netherlands also placed an order for 60 vehicles, to be fitted with a domestically produced Hollandse Signaa-

In World War II the German army made extensive use of anti-aircraft guns mounted on tank chassis to provide immediate air defence to its armoured units. The Gepard is the modern West German army's equivalent, and combines a Swiss-developed radar and gun system with the proven chassis of a Leopard I Main Battle Tank.

Gepard's firepower is provided by a pair of Oerlikon 35-mm KDA cannon. This is a popular anti-aircraft weapon and is seen here in the Marconi Marksman anti-aircraft turret, fitted in this case to a T-55 hull. The Oerlikon cannon fires a wide variety of ammunition.

lapparaten integrated search and tracking radar.

The all-welded hull is almost identical to that of the Leopard 1 Main Battle Tank, the major modification being a 95 hp auxiliary diesel engine forward of the turret. The driver is seated at the front, right-hand side of the hull, with a one-piece hatch cover that opens to the right.

When operating, closed-down vision is provided by three periscopes, one of which can be replaced by an infra-red periscope for night driving. The remaining two crew members are seated forward in the large cast turret, beneath a one-piece hatch. Both the commander and gunner are provided with a fully stabilized panoramic telescope for target acquisition, observation purposes and for laying the gun against ground targets.

Powerpack

The extremely reliable MTU MB 838 Ca. M500 10-cylinder, multi-fuel engine develops 830hp at 2,200 rpm and is located with the transmission at the rear. The engine cowling is so well designed that a trained team of engineers can remove and replace a complete engine under field conditions in less than 30 minutes, considerably reducing the Gepard's vulnerability.

The Model 2F4 HP250 transmission, manufactured by Zahnradfabrik Friedrichshafen AF, has a four-speed, planetary-gear shift, with an electro-

Mounted on the back of the turret is the pulse-Doppler search radar, which scans the surrounding airspace out to 15 km. It can be folded down flush with the top of the turret to reduce the vehicle's height.

hydraulically operated, torque converter lock-up clutch. This excellent combination allows Gepard to travel at speeds of up to 64 kph on rough tracks, climb gradients of 60 per cent and overcome vertical obstacles of 1.15 metres. This is a major feature, considering that any future European war is likely to be fought at great speed over vast areas, making it crucial for an anti-aircraft system to be able to keep up with the tanks and armoured personnel carriers it is protecting.

Suspension

Suspension is of the torsion-bar type, with seven road wheels, an idler at the front, drive sprocket at the rear, and four track support rollers. Despite the comparatively large hull, steering is made easy by a two-radius, cross-

drive steering transmission, with variable radii for flat bends and speed-dependent radii for sharp bends.

Firepower

Firepower is provided by twin Swiss 35-mm Oerlikon KDA cannons. Each gun has a cyclic rate of 550 rounds per minute, and can fire single shots, bursts or continuously. Although this high rate of fire is excellent, only 310 APHE anti-aircraft rounds per gun are carried. Ammunition conservation is a perennial problem. The empty magazines take between 20 and 30 minutes to reload, leaving crucial periods when Gepard is unoperational. Each cannon is independently belt-fed, the empty cartridge cases being automatically ejected without breaking the NBC protective seal.

The guns have an effective operational range of 4,000 metres, at which distance there is a 75 per cent chance

Twin 35-mm cannon point menacingly skyward after the radar's IFF (Identification Friend or Foe) system identifies a contact as hostile. The tracking radar now guides the guns on target while the search radar continues to scan for other targets.

Radar systems

The vehicle has a vehicle navigation system so the screen of the radar is always oriented north. The search radar operates in the E/F bands and alerts the crew if there is a contact. The Siemens-Albis pulse-Doppler tracking radar, which operates in the J band, can immediately track a target within 200 degrees.

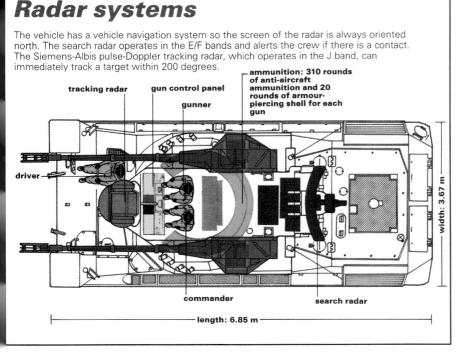

tracking radar   gun control panel

gunner

ammunition: 310 rounds of anti-aircraft ammunition and 20 rounds of armour-piercing shell for each gun

driver

width: 3.67 m

commander   search radar

length: 6.85 m

Inside the Gepard

In service with West Germany, Belgium and the Netherlands, Gepard is a highly successful anti-aircraft gun, although it badly needs higher velocity ammunition and some way of speeding up the time spent re-loading.

The Netherlands brought 95 Gepards between 1977 and 1979, and they can be distinguished by the different search radar on the back of the turret. Hollandse-Signaalapparaten provided both search and tracking radars on the Dutch vehicles.

35-mm Oerlikon cannon
These fire at a cyclic rate of 550 rounds per minute and feed from chutes which are separated from the fighting compartment. Depending on the range and the type of target, the computer will select bursts of between 20 and 40 rounds.

Tracking radar
When not in action, this can be rotated 180 degrees so that the antenna is facing the turret.

Driver
He enters and exits via a single-piece hatch cover which opens to the left.

of a direct hit. Each projectile weighs 550g, and although a single hit would probably not destroy a modern Soviet jet, it would probably cause sufficient damage to force the pilot to abort his mission. Hits on any moving part of a helicopter would ruin the pilot's day.

Gepard has a secondary anti-tank, direct-fire role for which it carries a mixture of 40 HEAT (High Explosive Anti-Tank) and AP-T, (Armour Piercing-Tracer) rounds externally in an armoured magazine. Although the turret has full 360° power traverse, elevation of 85° and depression of −5°, enabling swift gun manoeuvrability, its effect against the latest Warsaw Pact tanks would be minimal. Also, Gepard's basic armour plating would offer little protection against the 125-mm guns of most Soviet tanks. So Gepard's usefulness in ground combat would be limited.

Target acquisition

Gepard has one of the finest tracking radars in existence, with an azimuth acquisition speed of 90 degrees per second and elevation acquisition speed of 42 degrees per second.

The search radar, which can be operated while the vehicle is travelling, is mounted on the turret rear. It sweeps through 360°, and can be folded down to reduce the vehicle's height to three metres when not in use. As soon as an aircraft approaches within 15 km an alarm sounds and the aircraft's position is highlighted on the screen. If a number of aircraft approach, the radar computer assesses the greatest threat and marks it on the screen. Details can then be transmitted to air-defence headquarters, if necessary.

If the target does not respond to the IFF (Identification Friend or Foe) system integrated into the search radar, the Ku-Band pulse-Doppler tracking radar at the front of the turret, automatically acquires and tracks the target. The tracking radar, which sweeps through approximately 200°, can be traversed through 180° so that the front faces the front of the turret.

Like most self-propelled anti-aircraft guns, Gepard can blast off all its ammunition in under a minute. Unfortunately, re-loading takes at least 20 minutes.

Leopard 1 chassis
The chassis is a modified version of the Leopard 1 tank chassis. It is fractionally longer and the armour thickness has been reduced.

Finally, the main computer calculates the exact firing position and number of rounds required. A stand-by computer, linked to the 95 hp auxiliary diesel engine, is provided in case the main computer fails.

Ironically, the otherwise excellent search radar can create problems. The large dish, which rotates continuously and stands some 1.03 metres above the turret, must be allowed to

Air Defence with the Gepard

Gunner
Both the commander and gunner observe through a stabilized panoramic telescopic sight with a magnification of × 1.5 or × 6. They have sun filters, de-icers, de-misters and screen washers and wipers.

Commander
The telescopic sights provided for commander and gunner enable the crew to engage targets visually rather than using the radar, or to acquire them visually and then use radar only for the engagement. This reduces the risk of the vehicle being detected by its radar emissions.

Search radar
The telltale dish rotates at 60 revolutions a minute and increases the height of the Gepard by a nearly 50 per cent. When not in use it can be folded backwards to lie flush with the top of the turret.

The prominent search radar dish rotates once a second, but adds a metre to the vehicle's height. It is practically impossible to camouflage convincingly.

raverse freely, so camouflage is difficult. Although reconnaissance troops okingly refer to sightings of "haystacks" surmounted by spinning radar dishes, the problem is a serious one. Gepard is associated with regimental and divisional headquarters, so a tell-tale sighting can invite an enemy attack.

Gepard also has an excellent navigational system, both for cross-country exercises and to ensure that the screens are constantly orientated to the north.

The future

Despite the obvious success of Gepard, with the exception of the virtually identical Cheetah, it remains the only self-propelled anti-aircraft gun system within the NATO arsenal. Attempts by the United States to

While the British Army relies exclusively on missiles for air defence, the West Germans use a more sensible mixture. Gepard is supplemented by Roland SAMs mounted on the chassis of Marder APCs.

introduce a system on the cheap by amalgamating an existing 40-mm Bofors gun, M48 tank chassis and F16 aircraft radar failed disastrously.

Similarly, virtually all Warsaw Pact members rely on the highly successful ZSU-23-4 to provide their air defence cover. Although over 30 years old in design, the ZSU-23-4 is universally respected and feared by all pilots forced to fly anywhere near it, and it is likely to remain in service for many years to come. However, open source Intelligence reports suggest that a new 30-mm twin-barrelled self-propelled anti-aircraft gun is due to enter service soon.

NATO surface-to-air policy is pre-

Battlefield Evaluation: comparing

Gepard

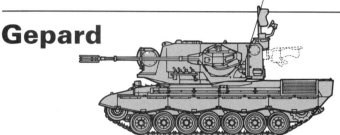

Firing at a cyclic rate of 550 rounds per minute, the Gepard's twin Oerlikon 35-mm cannon armament is capable of bringing down any known ground attack aircraft. The improvement programme involves the use of higher velocity ammunition, linkage to an external search radar unit and new fire control systems. A thermal imager is also planned to reduce radar emissions from the vehicle which can be detected by the enemy.

Specification:
Crew: 3
Combat weight: 47 tonnes
Road speed: 65 km/h
Length: 6.85 m
Height: (radar up) 4.03 m
Armament: 2×35-mm cannon

Assessment
Firepower   ★★★★
Accuracy   ★★★★
Age   ★★★★
Worldwide users   ★★

The Gepard is the most successful NATO self-propelled anti-aircraft gun system.

ZSU-23-4 and ZSU-30-2

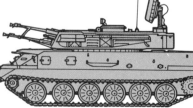

The ZSU-23-4 remains the standard Warsaw Pact self-propelled anti-aircraft gun, but its replacement is believed to have entered service during the early 1980s. Its successor, to be designated the ZSU-30-2, is believed to be armed with twin 30-mm cannon, which may be related to the 30-mm cannon fitted to BMP-2 MICVs. The chassis may be that of a T-72. Meanwhile the ZSU-23-4 is still a powerful weapon, and improvements to its fire control system will make it even more dangerous to NATO aircraft.

Specification:
(ZSU-23-4)
Crew: 4
Combat weight: 20.5 tonnes
Road speed: 44 km/h
Length: 6.54 m
Height: 3.8 m
Armament: 4×23-mm cannon

Assessment
Firepower   ★★★★★
Accuracy   ★★★
Age   ★★★★
Worldwide users   ★★★★

This is a Pentagon artist's impression of the Soviet successor to the ZSU-23-4 system.

Wildcat

Wildcat is an excellent self-propelled anti-aircraft system because the customer has a wide choice of different versions, ranging from the basic to the all-weather, day/night system. The radar incorporates an automatic IFF system, and friendly and enemy aircraft are shown differently on the operator's screen. The duration of the 30-mm cannon bursts is controlled by the computer after it has evaluated all target data.

Specification:
Crew: 3
Combat weight: 18.5 tonnes
Road speed: 80 km/h
Length: 6.88 m
Height: 2.74 m
Armament: 2×30-mm cannon

Assessment
Firepower   ★★★
Accuracy   ★★★★
Age   ★
Worldwide users   —

Wildcat is a very cost-effective system tailored to meet different requirements and defence budgets.

sently in a state of flux. Excellent short-range, hand-held missiles such as Blowpipe, Javelin and Stinger are now common among front-line units, and belts of Patriot missiles offer some long-range protection to airfields and other key installations. However, medium-range protection (3 to 5 km) is sadly lacking. The British Rapier and French Roland II are both excellent, but there are not enough of them. Gun systems are cheaper to produce, equip and maintain than SAMs, and Gepard proves how successful they can be. It is highly likely, therefore, that far from being phased out, the gun will co-exist with the missile for many decades to come.

Fitted to a lightened version of the Leopard I tank chassis, the Gepard has the cross-country mobility to keep up with German armoured units. It can be used in the ground role but it would be foolish to do so except in self-defence.

the Gepard with its rivals

M-163 Vulcan

This combination of a 20-mm Gatling gun on an M113 chassis is now going to be replaced by an M2 Bradley equipped with a 25-mm Bushmaster cannon and an ADATS missile launcher. The latter is a Swiss surface-to-air missile which can also be used against ground targets between 500 and 8000 metres from the launcher. Flying at Mach 3 and capable of penetrating 900mm of armour plate, it is a very useful missile.

Specification: (M-163)
Crew: 4
Combat weight: 12 tonnes
Road speed: 67 km/h
Length: 4.86 m
Height: 2.7 m
Armament: 1×6 barrel 20-mm cannon

Assessment
Firepower ★★★★
Accuracy ★★
Age ★★★★★
Worldwide users ★★

Vulcan's replacement has at last been chosen, but it will remain in service for several years yet.

M-42 Duster

The M-42 was the M-163's predecessor, in production from 1951 to 1956 and used in Vietnam in the ground role. Although replaced in the Regular Army, it soldiered on for many years in the National Guard and was exported to many countries including Austria, Greece, Japan, Jordan, Taiwan and Turkey. The 40-mm cannon are only capable of about 120 rounds per minute per barrel, and the system relies on visually tracking its target.

Specification:
Crew: 6
Combat weight: 22.4 tonnes
Road speed: 72 km/h
Length: 5.8 m
Height: 2.8 m
Armament: 2×40-mm cannon

Assessment
Firepower ★★
Accuracy ★
Age ★★★★★
Worldwide users ★★

The M42 was the first self-propelled AA gun used by the West German army during the 1950s.

V-300

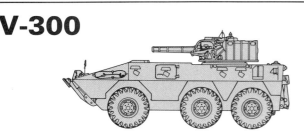

Several models of the Cadillac Gage Commando APC are available as air defence vehicles armed with the same weapons system as the M-163. Saudi Arabia has bought a number of V-150 Commandos with the 20-mm Vulcan cannon installed and three hydraulic jacks fitted to the vehicle to stabilize it when firing. Cadillac Gage now advertises the six-wheeled V-300 as a potential anti-aircraft vehicle.

Specification: (V-150 version)
Crew: 4
Combat weight: 10.2 tonnes
Road speed: 88 km/h
Length: 5.68 m
Height: 2.54 m
Armament: 1×6 barrel 20-mm cannon

Assessment
Firepower ★★★★
Accuracy ★★
Age ★
Worldwide users ★

Vulcan is now offered as a 'drop-in' system for fitting to vehicles in the Commando APC series.

Italy's Chic Shooter

The Italian army was among the first people to use sub-machine guns, and Beretta the second people to make them. The Italians devised a very light machine-gun firing 9-mm pistol ámmunition in 1917, but in its original form it was somewhat impractical. So Beretta took the basic receiver, barrel and mechanism, allied it to a conventional carbine stock, and produced the Beretta M1918 sub-machine gun. With one or two subsequent modifications this remained in Italian service right

The above, armed with Beretta PM 12 sub-machine guns, 9-mm pistols and bayonets, are actually police officers of a specialist branch of the Italian Carabinieri known as the 'Nucleo Operativo Centrale Di Sicurezze', or NOCS for short. They are on counter-terrorist exercises in Sardinia.

Specialist accessories

A high-power illuminator grip with rechargeable battery is available for fighting through a house in darkness. Note the trigger for switching the light on at the required moment.

Night vision scopes such as third-generation image intensifiers can be fitted for night fighting: a very handy package for close target recce and other patrolling tasks.

through World War II, but few people realised, since it looked like just another short rifle.

Post-war weapons

Tullo Marengoni, the Beretta designer who devised the M1918, subsequently developed a number of submachine guns following the M1918; these were very successful and efficient weapons. But in the early 1950s a new designer, Domenico Salza, took a fresh look at the submachine gun idea and began putting

together some experimental models. These led to the Model 12, which went into production in 1959 and was adopted by the Italian army in 1961.

The Model 12 was a very up-to-date design, employing stamped metal pressings which are spot-welded together to form the receiver, magazine housing and trigger housing. The whole design was geared to make manufacture quick, cheap and easy and to produce a reliable gun. In order to get as compact a weapon as possible, Salza adopted the 'overhung bolt' or 'telescoping bolt' idea; most of the length of the barrel lies inside the receiver, and the cylindrical bolt is hollowed out for much of its length so that when forward it encloses the rear of the barrel. The sides of the bolt are slotted so that the cartridge can be fed and the empty case ejected, and the cocking handle is fitted to its front end, protruding through a slot in the receiver.

The Beretta is an extremely compact weapon due to the telescoping bolt design. It can be fired with the stock folded on semi-auto like an overfed pistol with reasonable accuracy.

The advantage of this 'telescoping bolt' design is that the gun's overall length is kept short, compared with the length of the barrel. In a conventional design the front of the bolt stops at the end of the barrel; there has to be a specific mass of bolt in order for the blowback system to work, and the bolt has to travel back a certain distance in the receiver to absorb the recoil and have enough room to extract, eject and reload.

Telescoping bolt

Add all these together and you finish up with a rather long weapon, which is why conventional submachine guns of this sort tend to have short barrels. But by telescoping the bolt around the barrel you can save

Beretta also offer a laser sighting system for the PM 12. The laser is especially useful for the police: the target can see a dot on him marking the impact point, with obvious deterrent effect.

The silencer requires a special barrel for fitting. There is some noise as the bolt moves forward and back, but when being fired in short bursts the sound of the weapon is not recogniseable over 30 m.

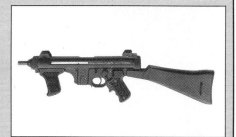

The stock is a little flimsy for some tasks, and a fixed stock variant is available for those looking for the really soldier-proof item.

Weapons and Equipment Guide

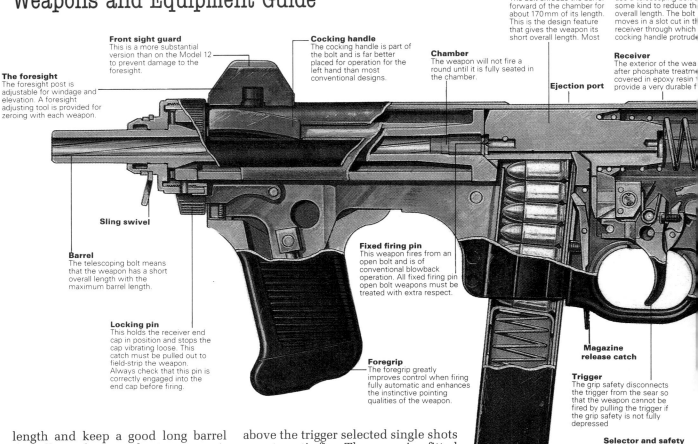

Front sight guard
This is a more substantial version than on the Model 12 to prevent damage to the foresight.

The foresight
The foresight post is adjustable for windage and elevation. A foresight adjusting tool is provided for zeroing with each weapon.

Cocking handle
The cocking handle is part of the bolt and is far better placed for operation for the left hand than most conventional designs.

Chamber
The weapon will not fire a round until it is fully seated in the chamber.

Bolt
The bolt shrouds the barrel forward of the chamber for about 170mm of its length. This is the design feature that gives the weapon its short overall length. Most

modern sub-machine g use a telescoping bolt o some kind to reduce th overall length. The bolt moves in a slot cut in th receiver through which cocking handle protrud

Ejection port

Receiver
The exterior of the wea after phosphate treatme covered in epoxy resin provide a very durable f

Sling swivel

Barrel
The telescoping bolt means that the weapon has a short overall length with the maximum barrel length.

Locking pin
This holds the receiver end cap in position and stops the cap vibrating loose. This catch must be pulled out to field-strip the weapon. Always check that this pin is correctly engaged into the end cap before firing.

Fixed firing pin
This weapon fires from an open bolt and is of conventional blowback operation. All fixed firing pin open bolt weapons must be treated with extra respect.

Foregrip
The foregrip greatly improves control when firing fully automatic and enhances the instinctive pointing qualities of the weapon.

Magazine release catch

Trigger
The grip safety disconnects the trigger from the sear so that the weapon cannot be fired by pulling the trigger if the grip safety is not fully depressed

Selector and safety catch
The safety catch is conveniently under the thumb and has three positions: fully back, mark 'S' in white for safe, followed by '1' in red for semi-automatic fire, and finally all the way forward, marked 'R' in red for full auto.

Sear block
This holds the bolt to th rear when the weapon cocked and releases it v the grip safety is depres and the trigger is squee In semi-automatic mode sear engages the bolt, holding it to the rear aft each shot. On automati sear only engages the b when the trigger is rele

Magazine
The magazine holds 32 rounds of 9-mm Parabellum. It has round holes cut in the back, marked 32, 20 and 10, so you can visually check how much ammo you have left.

length and keep a good long barrel that allows the cartridge to get maximum velocity.

Another advantage claimed for this design is that the positioning of the barrel and bolt make for excellent balance, and it is quite easy to fire the M12 single-handed at full automatic without very much 'climb' of the muzzle.

The M12 had a pistol grip which carried a grip safety; this has to be squeezed by the firing hand before the bolt is released, preventing accidental discharges. There was also a push-through safety catch above the grip which additionally locked the grip safety. Another push-through button

above the trigger selected single shots or automatic fire. The magazine fitted into a housing just ahead of the trigger, and a front grip gave a good holding position. There was a folding metal stock which lay alongside the receiver when folded.

Military and police use

The M12 sold well in the 1960s and was adopted by military and police forces all over the world, and in the middle 1970s the Model 12S appeared. Although this looks the same as the Model 12 there are some important improvements.

The first and most important change lay in the safety and selective-

Field stripping the Model 12S

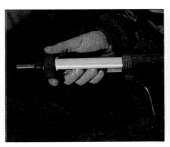

1 Remove the magazine by pressing on the magazine release catch, which is located forward of the trigger guard.

2 Grasp the cocking handle with the forefinger and thumb and rack it back to eyeball the chamber. Remember, this weapon fires from an open bolt, so every time the bolt goes forward, if there is ammo there it will fire it.

3 Pull down the catch underneath the knurled locking receiver cap at the front of the weapon. Unscrew the ring to release the bolt and barrel assembly.

4 The bolt and barrel assembly will slide out of the weapon forwards and then separate the locking receiver cap from the barrel.

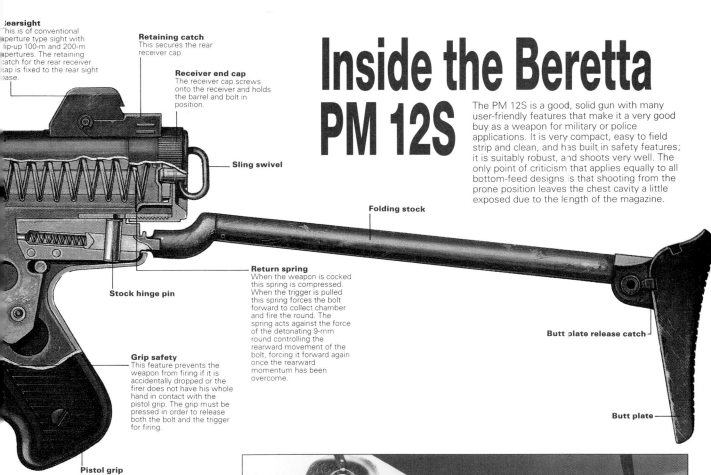

Rearsight
This is of conventional aperture type sight with flip-up 100-m and 200-m apertures. The retaining catch for the rear receiver cap is fixed to the rear sight base.

Retaining catch
This secures the rear receiver cap.

Receiver end cap
The receiver cap screws onto the receiver and holds the barrel and bolt in position.

Sling swivel

Folding stock

Stock hinge pin

Return spring
When the weapon is cocked this spring is compressed. When the trigger is pulled this spring forces the bolt forward to collect chamber and fire the round. The spring acts against the force of the detonating 9-mm round controlling the rearward movement of the bolt, forcing it forward again once the rearward momentum has been overcome.

Grip safety
This feature prevents the weapon from firing if it is accidentally dropped or the firer does not have his whole hand in contact with the pistol grip. The grip must be pressed in order to release both the bolt and the trigger for firing.

Pistol grip

Butt plate release catch

Butt plate

Inside the Beretta PM 12S

The PM 12S is a good, solid gun with many user-friendly features that make it a very good buy as a weapon for military or police applications. It is very compact, easy to field strip and clean, and has built in safety features; it is suitably robust, and shoots very well. The only point of criticism that applies equally to all bottom-feed designs is that shooting from the prone position leaves the chest cavity a little exposed due to the length of the magazine.

A Beretta Model 12 is test-fired on the factory testing range at the Beretta plant at Gardone. This model sold very well throughout the 1950s.

Below: The telescoping bolt fits around the barrel to give the gun maximum barrel length for minimum overall length.

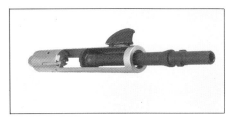

5 To remove the barrel from the bolt assembly, tip the barrel up and withdraw it to the rear.

6 Lift up the catch to the rear of the rear sight to release the locking receiver cap.

7 Unscrew the locking receiver cap in the same way as on the front of the weapon. Remember, this cap is under spring pressure, so take care when removing it.

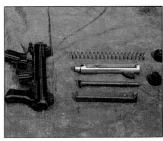

8 Withdraw the recoil spring to complete the field strip. The design makes the weapon simple to strip and easy to clean, with no small pieces to lose.

Above: The sub-machine gun can be converted into a teargas grenade launcher with a different recoil spring and rear receiver cap and special propulsive ammunition.

fire arrangements. Instead of two separate controls, a single rotary switch lever was placed on the left side of the receiver, giving safe/single shot/automatic in one movement. The grip safety was still fitted to the pistol grip, but the rest of the selection could be done with the thumb. The foresight was made adjustable for both elevation and windage; both sights were

Left: The Beretta's vertical foregrip, reminiscent of the 1928 Thompson, is a great help in controlling muzzle climb and producing bursts on target. The design is also a departure from current trends in not having the magazine seated in the pistol grip.

Battlefield Evaluation: comparing

Beretta PM 12

Sub-machine guns are glamour weapons. New designs seem to appear every month and disappear just as fast. As a result there are a score or more which can be compared with the Beretta. Like the Model 12S, the weapons discussed here are likely to be around for many years.

Specification:
Cartridge: 9-mm Parabellum
Weight: 3.2 kg empty
Length: (stock folded) 418 mm
Cyclic rate of fire: 550/650 rounds per minute.
Magazine: 32-round box

Assessment
Reliability ★★★★★
Accuracy ★★★★
Age ★★★★
Worldwide users ★★★

Beretta products have always been good quality and the PM 12S is an excellent weapon.

Steyr MPi69

Very similar to the Beretta, the MPi69 is another pressed-steel design with an 'overhung' bolt. The bolt has a large proportion of its length above and ahead of the bolt face so that it lies along the top of the barrel when the bolt is closed. This, like the telescoped bolt, makes for a compact weapon. The Steyr design is well made and an exceptionally long barrel helps accuracy. It is available in silenced form and there is a special version for firing from within APCs.

Specification:
Cartridge: 9-mm Parabellum
Weight: (32-round magazine) 3.55 kg
Length: 465 mm with butt retracted
Cyclic rate of fire: 550 rounds per minute.
Magazine: 25- or 32-round box

Assessment
Reliability ★★★★★
Accuracy ★★★★
Age ★★★★
Worldwide users ★★

The MPi69 has a conventional cocking handle, making it a very sound and accurate weapon.

Heckler & Koch MP5

One of the most popular and widely used designs, the MP5 is different from the ordinary run of SMGs in being a delayed blowback weapon, firing from a closed bolt. This, together with a 225 mm barrel gives it the edge in accuracy although it makes the mechanism somewhat complicated. Another unusual feature is the ability to fire three-round bursts for a single press on the trigger.

Specification:
Cartridge: 9-mm Parabellum
Weight: (30-round magazine) 3 kg
Length: 490 mm with stock retracted
Cyclic rate of fire: 800 rounds per minute.
Magazine: 15- or 30-round box

Assessment
Reliability ★★★★★
Accuracy ★★★★★
Age ★★★★
Worldwide users ★★★★★

The MP5 is perhaps the easiest sub-machine gun to learn to shoot well with, as it fires from a closed bolt.

given stronger bases and better side protection; and the catch that holds the rear body cap in place was moved from the bottom of the receiver to the top, so that it could be operated more easily when stripping and could be inspected easily to ensure that the cap was tight. The folding stock was improved, the internal mechanism of the trigger was improved, and the exterior of the weapon was finished with a coating of epoxy resin instead of the earlier phosphate finish.

The Model 12S has replaced the earlier M12 in the Italian army and police, and is in use with several other armies around the world. It is also made under licence in Brazil.

The PM 12S shoots well, and three- to five-round bursts can easily be kept on a Figure 11 target. Deliberate shooting from the standing position at 50 metres produces a 25-cm group. The gun compares very favourably with more expensive and complicated designs such as the Heckler & Koch.

the Beretta PM 12S with its rivals

UZI

Universally considered 'the one to beat', the UZI has been around for a long time but is still a type leader. Of simple construction, it has a telescoping bolt to give compactness and the magazine's location in the pistol grip gives it excellent balance. Like the MP5 there are some variants – the Mini-UZI and the Micro-UZI – as well as a semi-automatic version for police use.

Specification:
Cartridge: 9-mm Parabellum
Weight: (32-round magazine) 4.1 kg
Length: (stock folded) 470 mm
Cyclic rate of fire: 600 rounds per minute.
Magazine: 25- or 32-round box

Assessment
Reliability   ★★★★★
Accuracy   ★★★★
Age   ★★★★★
Worldwide users   ★★★★★

Competition in the market place is hot, and there are rumours that IMI are working on a new Uzi.

Star Z-84

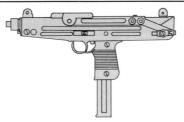

This is the Spanish Army's latest sub-machine gun, and one which will doubtless find a ready market in Latin American countries. With the magazine in the pistol grip, it resembles the UZI in appearance but the interior is completely different. It uses a recessed telescoping bolt which rides on a set of rails inside the receiver. There is ample clearance all round so it will continue to function in the presence of dirt and dust. It has an automatic safety preventing the bolt from moving unless the weapon is being fired.

Specification:
Cartridge: 9-mm Parabellum
Weight: 3 kg empty
Length: (stock folded) 410 mm
Cyclic rate of fire: 600 rounds per minute.
Magazine: 25-round box

Assessment
Reliability   ★★★★★
Accuracy   ★★★★
Age   ★
Worldwide users   ★

Some Spanish guns have had a bad press. Certainly the Z-84 is cheap and entirely adequate.

Sterling L2A3

The oldest sub-machine gun in regular service, the Sterling dates back to 1944 when the first ones were tested 'for real' at Arnhem. Of conventional, not to say old fashioned design, the Sterling is reliable and tough, which accounts for its continuing employment in some 90 different countries. There are numerous variant models for use by Police and Special Forces and, like the Steyr, there is a silenced model available.

Specification:
Cartridge: 9-mm Parabellum
Weight: 3.5 kg
Length: (stock folded) 480 mm
Cyclic rate of fire: 550 rounds per minute.
Magazine: 34-round box

Assessment
Reliability   ★★★★★
Accuracy   ★★★★
Age   ★★★★★
Worldwide users   ★★★★★

The Sterling will be replaced in service use by SA 80, but will soldier on in Territorial Army units.

On the Gunline with the M 109

Well used artillery causes more casualties to the enemy, and has a greater adverse effect on his will to fight, than any other weapon. No matter how capable the latest tanks and infantry weapons may be, neither can hope to bring about victory if the enemy can bring down accurate artillery fire on their positions. But if artillery is to carry out its prime role of disrupting, demoralising and destroying the enemy it must have sufficient range and power to bring down concentrated fire on enemy positions.

The artillery's job has recently been made more difficult by the introduction of much improved tank armour. Only a few years ago a near miss from a 105 mm Abbot would have immobilized an enemy tank, but nothing less than a 155-mm gun can hope to have that effect against T-64s, T-72s or T-80s. Fortunately the venerable but reliable United States' M 109 howitzer adequately fills this role.

Production

The first production model of the M 109 was completed by the Cadillac Motor Car Division of General Motors in 1962. Since then some 3,700 models have been completed, 1,800 for United States Army service, the rest for export to over fifteen countries throughout Europe and the Middle East, making the M 109 the most widely used self-propelled howitzer in the world.

Design and equipment

Although the all-welded aluminium hull and turret provide the crew with protection against small arms fire, they are of little use against shrapnel. The comparatively short-ranged M 109 would be vulnerable to counter battery fire in an artillery duel with its Soviet divisional level equivalent, the 2S3.

Firepower

The stubby 155-mm L/23 howitzer has a distinctive smoke extractor approximately two-thirds of the way along the barrel. The semi-automatic breech block and hydro-pneumatic recoil system enable an astounding rate of fire of three rounds per minute to be attained over a short period. However the 43 kg shell is difficult to handle in the confined turret and crew fatigue reduces the practical rate of sustained fire to 45 rounds per hour. Furthermore as each gun carries only 28 rounds of ammunition, replenishment soon becomes a problem.

Variants

West Germany, Italy and Switzerland have produced their own variants of the original M 109, in each

case with an improved gunnery system. The West German M 109G has Rheinmetall horizontal sliding breech-block and locally-produced sights, enabling it to fire domestically-produced ammunition to a much increased range of 18,500 metres. The Italian variant, built under licence by OTO Melara, has a lengthened barrel to accept ammunition originally designed for the FH 70. Using standard ammunition, this has a range

*Used throughout **NATO**, the M109 will be modernised to serve until the end of the century. National rivalry within **NATO** seems to rule out a multinational replacement for this veteran self-propelled gun.*

On the Gunline with the M 109

The M109 fires 48-kg shells to a maximum range of 18 km. Rocket-assisted projectiles can increase the range of 24 km, but they wear out the barrel quickly. British and American M109s carry tactical nuclear shells at the moment, although they may be negotiated away.

of 24,000 metres. The Swiss, with an eye to fire and movement rather than range, have fitted a semi-automatic loader to their variant, designated M 109U, to increase the rate of fire to six rounds per minute.

M 109 A1/A2

Attempts were made throughout the 1970s to build a joint European replacement for the M 109. The new gun, provisionally named SP 70, with

The British Army of the Rhine has about 100 M109s in service. They provide a powerful reserve of firepower to support the infantry and armour but must 'shoot and scoot' to avoid enemy counter-battery fire.

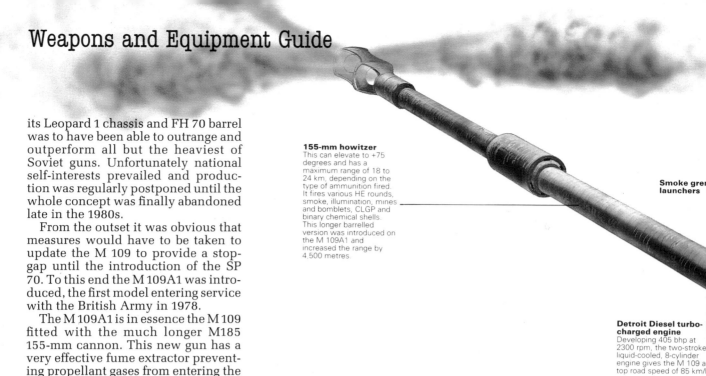

its Leopard 1 chassis and FH 70 barrel was to have been able to outrange and outperform all but the heaviest of Soviet guns. Unfortunately national self-interests prevailed and production was regularly postponed until the whole concept was finally abandoned late in the 1980s.

From the outset it was obvious that measures would have to be taken to update the M 109 to provide a stop-gap until the introduction of the SP 70. To this end the M 109A1 was introduced, the first model entering service with the British Army in 1978.

The M 109A1 is in essence the M 109 fitted with the much longer M185 155-mm cannon. This new gun has a very effective fume extractor preventing propellant gases from entering the turret after firing, takes a bigger charge and offers a greater maximum range of 18,000 metres compared with 14,700 metres of the standard M 109.

The M 109A2 has an improved shell rammer and recoil mechanism, an M178 modified gun mount and other minor improvements. To date there are 101 M 109A1s/A2s in service with Royal Artillery Medium Regiments, based mainly in West Germany.

155-mm howitzer
This can elevate to +75 degrees and has a maximum range of 18 to 24 km, depending on the type of ammunition fired. It fires various HE rounds, smoke, illumination, mines and bomblets, CLGP and binary chemical shells. This longer barrelled version was introduced on the M 109A1 and increased the range by 4,500 metres.

Smoke grenade launchers

Detroit Diesel turbo-charged engine
Developing 405 bhp at 2300 rpm, the two-stroke liquid-cooled, 8-cylinder engine gives the M 109 a top road speed of 85 km/h

M 992 FAASV
Based on the chassis of the M 109, M992s carry 93 155-mm shells, 99 propellant charges and 104 fuses. It loads ammunition into an M 109 along a conveyor belt at a rate of about eight rounds a minute. This is a valuable asset, allowing a battery to quickly replenish its ammunition supply and relocate to avoid enemy fire.

Aluminium hull

Driver

Periscope

The future

The future of the M 109 was assured in September 1985, when the United States Government awarded a $53 million contract for the production of the M 109A5 under its Howitzer Improvement Programme (HIP). Under that contract, 11 existing M 109s are being converted, nine for the US Army and two for Israel.

Numerous improvements are being made to the M 109 HIP. A new aluminium armoured turret will have additional storage for 36 charges, whilst a

*Inside an M109 the fumes build up rapidly and you have to leave the rear door open to breathe properly. If the enemy were to use chemical weapons the crew would have to wear **NBC** suits and the rate of fire would fall off sharply.*

Inside the M 109

The M 109 plays a key role in the defence of Western Europe. Highly mobile to avoid enemy counter-battery fire, its 155-mm gun provides vital fire support for NATO infantry. Used by most NATO armies, the example illustrated belongs to the US Army. In the background, another M 109 replenishes its ammunition from an M992 Field Artillery Ammunition Support Vehicle (FAASV).

.50-cal Browning machine-gun
This is pintle-mounted on the front of the commander's cupola on the right-hand side of the turret. Its primary function is for anti-aircraft fire; if the commander finds himself engaging enemy infantry with it, the M 109 is in serious trouble.

Gunner
In addition to the gunner, the turret contains the commander and three ammunition handlers.

istic sight

amic

Elevation quadrant

Weapon accumulator

Breech

Turret ring

Shell racks

Hydraulic system

Stowage bins

Rear access door
This has to remain open when in action because the turret quickly fills with fumes despite the new fume extractors fitted on the M 109A1. The keenly awaited M 109A5s will have an NBC system able to ventilate the turret so that the vehicle can fire while closed down.

Shell bins

Conveyor belt for handling shells

Spade
Manually lowered into the ground before firing, this helps keep the M 109 steady when in action.

combination of a new Emerson Electric automatic loader and Honeywell modular automatic fire-control system allows for burst fire of three rounds in 15 seconds, followed by a sustained rate of 8 rpm – far superior to anything in present-day service. Equally important for crew comfort, the NBC protection system will operate during firing; at present the M 109 is forced to fire with its rear door open. The M 109HIP will mount the improved 155-mm, 39 calibre gun although this may be replaced in the

Original M109s can be distinguished by the stubby L/23 barrel with the prominent smoke extractor behind the muzzle brake. It fires the basic High Explosive round 14,600 metres.

future by a 45 calibre tube with an estimated range of 38,000 metres, greater than the majority of 203-mm heavy guns in existence. This, however, remains for the future, as the much larger and more powerful gun will require a reinforced chassis and suspension.

If the M 109A5 HIP proves as effective as is anticipated, the United States will convert 1,700 models over five years, and Israel its entire arsenal of 450.

Austrian Army M109s in firing position. The normal rate of fire is about one round per minute, but up to three rounds a minute can be maintained for a short period.

Battlefield Evaluation: comparing

M 109

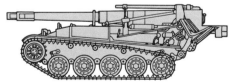

Now operated by 15 nations, the M 109 is the most successful post-war SP gun. Cheap to produce and easy to convert, it has provided artillery standardization seen nowhere else in NATO. The M 109A5 due to enter service in 1988 will outrange all but the largest Warsaw Pact guns. Even if Europe does manage to produce a new SP howitzer in the next few years, the M 109 will remain the principle NATO medium howitzer for a long time to come.

Specification:
Crew: 6
Combat weight: 25 tonnes
Road speed: 56 km/h
Power to weight ratio: 16 hp/tonne
Length: 6.1 m
Height: 2.8 m
Armament: 1×155-mm howitzer; 1×12.7 or 7.62-mm machine-gun

Assessment
Firepower	★★★★
Range	★★★
Age	★★★★★
Worldwide users	★★★★★

The M109 is the most widely used self-propelled gun outside the Warsaw Pact.

F3 155-mm

The F3 was developed in the 1950s and has been exported to Latin America and the Middle East. It still serves with the French army, although it is being replaced with the GCT 155-mm gun on an AMX-30 chassis. The F3 uses an AMX-13 light tank chassis with the rear idler removed but, being nearly 2½ tonnes heavier, it is not as agile as the tank. The standard HE projectile weighs 43.75 kg and has a range of 20 km.

Specification:
Crew: (on the weapon) 2
Combat weight: 17.4 tonnes
Road speed: 64 km/h
Power to weight ratio: 16 hp/tonne
Length: 6.2 m
Height: 2.08 m
Armament: 1×155-mm howitzer

Assessment
Firepower	★★★
Range	★★★
Age	★★★★★
Worldwide users	★★★

Vulnerable to counter-battery fire and NBC weapons, the F3 is being replaced by the GCT 155-mm gun.

2S3

The 2S3 appeared in 1973 and heralded a new generation of Soviet tracked artillery. Very little about this howitzer is new; the 152-mm gun was first used on the D-20 towed howitzer and the chassis is the same one used by the SA-4 'Ganef'. The only significant modification is the fume extractor fitted to the barrel to keep the gases out of the turret. Unlike the M 109, the 2S3 carries an anti-tank round which will penetrate 130-mm of armour at 1,000 metres.

Specification:
Crew: 6
Combat weight: 23 tonnes
Road speed: 55 km/h
Power to weight ratio: unknown
Length: 7.1 m
Height: 2.7 m
Armament: 1×152-mm howitzer; 1×7.62-mm machine-gun

Assessment
Firepower	★★★★
Protection	★★★
Age	★★
Worldwide users	★★

The Soviets lagged far behind in SP guns until the appearance of their 122-mm and 152-mm guns.

The M 109 is far less costly than any of its counterparts. It has enabled standardization of medium artillery within NATO, and has offered many countries which would not otherwise have been able to afford it the possibility of purchasing a large arsenal of self-propelled guns, and to modernize them at minimum cost.

The M 109 will go down in the history of armament as one of the best, long-lived and important contributions to the defence of NATO.

The US Army plans to field over 3,000 of the improved M109A2, which carries more ammunition and a better rammer and recoil system. The British Army acquired 69 M109A2s during 1981.

the M 109 with its rivals

G-6

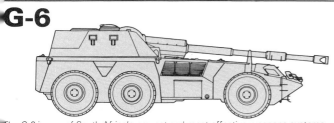

The G-6 is one of South Africa's newest and most effective weapons systems. Equipped with satellite navigation equipment, small groups of G-6s inflicted heavy losses on Angolan forces in 1987 from ranges of 40 km. By frequently moving to new firing positions they avoided FAPLA counter-battery fire while subjecting the enemy to devastating air-burst salvos. In common with modern South African vehicles, the G-6 uses a wheeled chassis which is more suited to long-range bush warfare than a tracklayer.

Specification:
Crew: 6
Combat weight: 36.5 tonnes
Road speed: 90 km/h
Power to weight ratio: 14 hp/tonne
Length: 10.4 m
Height: 3.1 m
Armament: 1×155-mm howitzer; 1×12.7-mm machine-gun; 3 weapons ports for crew personal weapons

Assessment
Firepower	★★★★
Range	★★★★★
Age	★★
Worldwide users	★

Very long-ranged and highly mobile, the South African G6 is one of the newest and best SP guns available.

M 107

Although the US, Italian and Dutch armies have converted their M 107s to M 110 standard, it remains in service with many other NATO forces including West Germany, Greece, Turkey and the UK. Some were sold to Iran before the revolution and may still be in service. The 175-mm ammunition is separate-loading and normal rate of fire is one round in two minutes. However, it can fire two rounds a minute for brief periods.

Specification:
Crew: (on the vehicle) 5
Combat weight: 28 tonnes
Road speed: 56 km/h
Power to weight ratio: 14.3 hp/tonne
Length: 5.7 m
Height: 3.6 m
Armament: 1×175-mm gun

Assessment
Firepower	★★★★★
Range	★★★★★
Age	★★★★
Worldwide users	★★★

The M107's intermediate-calibre armament has fallen from favour with the US Army.

M110

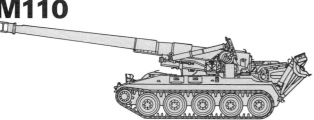

The standard NATO heavy self-propelled gun, the M110 provides concentrated firepower at corps level and the ability to retaliate if the Warsaw Pact use chemical or nuclear battlefield weapons. Its standard shells weigh over 90 kg and have a range of 16,800 metres. Two rounds are carried on the vehicle and the rest in an M548 cargo carrier which also transports eight members of the guncrew.

Specification:
Crew: 5
Combat weight: 28 tonnes
Road speed: 54 km/h
Power to weight ratio: 14 hp/tonne
Length: 5.7 m
Height: 2.9 m
Armament: 1×203-mm howitzer

Assessment
Firepower	★★★★★
Range	★★★★
Age	★★★★
Worldwide users	★★★

The M110 provides the heaviest artillery firepower available to NATO forces.

Advanced Tracking Techniques

Tracking involves more than just following a string of clues. You must constantly update and enhance your mental picture of the target until you can begin to predict his next move. This skill needs great concentration and attention to detail, and comes only with many hundreds of hours' practice.

If you have been practising the techniques already shown, you should now be following simple trails with some success. But there will still be questions: how old is the sign, how do I know the target wasn't walking backwards or with his shoes tied on back to front?

To answer any such questions when you are learning to track, you must return to ideal conditions. In your mind, build a picture of how the target you are following makes tracks under many varied circumstances. You can then adapt this to the more difficult conditions you face 90 per cent of the time. You will also need to experiment with the different soil and vegetation types in your locality to understand how they register the impression of a foot, and how they weather under different climatic conditions.

Reading a clear print

By now you know that clear prints are not the norm but occur sporadically along the trail, in places where the ground will accept a clear impression. These areas are known by trackers as 'track traps', and can be either natural track traps such as puddles and cowpats or man-made track traps:

Members of combat tracker team of the 4th Infantry Detachment load up for the return trip after an operation to locate Viet Cong who escaped an ambush somewhere in South Vietnam.

A tracking team working as a pair cuts for sign along the edges of the track. The tracking stick is dragged behind them to cancel what has already been covered.

When the team find good sign of the target they mark up the foot size and pace interval on their tracking sticks. On an operation, flank protection would be deployed.

deliberately prepared patches of ground where the target or enemy troops have to pass or are likely to pass. Such ideal spots often contain a wealth of information, so get into the habit of using them.

The following are major features you will need to be aware of. To practise reading these signs, set yourself some problems under ideal conditions.

1 Lines of force

These show as ripples or fracture lines within the track. They radiate from the major point of contact in exactly the opposite direction to the direction of movement. The faster the target is travelling, the more force produced, the greater the lines of force, and the further back they occur. When a target is moving very fast, sprinting for example, the whole track impression can be thrown backwards, very often breaking up. Pay careful attention to these lines for both speed and direction.

2 Soil scatter

Soil is sometimes thrown out of tracks by being kicked or picked up by the foot. It is usually to be seen in front of the track, in line with the direction of travel. This is especially true of tracks in snow.

3 Risings

These are where the ground has risen outside the track in response to pressure generated within the track. They are caused by forces in a downward and horizontal direction – often sudden braking and acceleration.

4 Deep impressions

These indicate where the target has placed its whole weight within the track. Each represents a separate movement. By carrying out a comparison with your own tracks you will be able to determine whether or not the target is carrying a load. If so, and you are following the track for any length of time, you should expect to see the

There is an obvious track trap at the bottom of the hill, so one tracker stays on the trail of footprints while the second doubles forward to see if he can recognise the target's sign in the track trap.

Right: The second tracker has picked up the target's sign in the mud, and signals the first tracker to stop tracking and move forward. The first tracker overbounds to the next track trap and so the process continues.

Track traps can be natural or man-made. Here you can see jungle boot prints moving towards you, with dog prints crossing it from bottom right to top left.

This left foot print shows that the target is moving at speed. The heel has not touched the ground at all, showing that the target is sprinting on the balls of his feet.

The smooth-soled track indicated is actually fresher than the well-defined track above it. Be careful: some tread patterns look like they are weathered tracks when first made.

On soft ground like this a quick age comparison can be made using your thumb. You compare the fresh edges of the thumb print to the weathered edges of the footprint to get an idea of the age.

'put down marks' of Bergens or rifles.

There are many more signs to learn, such as twists and slides, but these are best learned by field practice. If the target decides to employ counter-tracking procedures, it is your attention to fine details that will win the day. When a target tries something devious most trackers sense that something is wrong, and then test their hunch by studying the fine nuances in the track.

Make plaster casts

To develop this sense for detail, make plaster casts of tracks; this will teach you to notice the finest sign. As an experiment, ask a team-mate to lay some clear tracks, imagining he has come to a path junction, and briefly cannot decide which path to take, before finally choosing one. Then carefully study the tracks. You should be able to detect the indecisions as a series of fine lines around walls of the relevant tracks.

Is he walking backwards?

One of the commonest problems a tracker faces is how to tell if the target is walking backwards or has tied his shoes on back to front. The simple answer here is that a tracker does not determine the direction of travel by the direction in which the tracks are pointing: instead he reads the sign within the track to determine the direction. *Regardless of which way the prints point*, the direction of travel

must be directly opposite to the lines of force; and this is usually corroborated by a soil scatter.

Has he changed shoes?

This is very difficult. Unless you find the signs of where the target changed his shoes, all you can do is to refer to your careful measurements of his stride and your appreciation of how he walks. If he tries to alter his gait, you may be able to detect this as an unnaturalness in the overall appearance of the trail, although this can be very difficult to determine.

If the target discovers that he is being trailed, he may take evasive action such as walking down roads, rock hopping or walking down the course of a stream. This should not pose too great a problem: cut for sign along both sides of the obstacle, and beware of a possible ambush.

Ageing

Determining the age of a set of tracks is a skill which is often neglected, even by good trackers. With practice and dedication you should be able to determine the age of a fresh track to within 15 minutes.

Tracks can last for years under the right circumstances. There are parts of the world where dinosaur tracks can be seen, perfectly preserved by fossilisation. But in general terms, a track begins to deteriorate as soon as it has been formed. The wind and other climatic factors gradually cause the pro-

Tracking using the overbounding technique is very fast, and exceptional levels of fitness are required by the team. The South Africans have several techniques, this bike unit being one of the more adventurous.

minent features to collapse until no fine detail remains: in fact, a track with very defined features, such as a heavily-soled boot, will collapse and disappear faster than the track of a smooth-soled shoe.

Tracks with well-defined features always appear to be fresher than smooth tracks. Make an impression with your thumb in the ground alongside the track so that you can see how the soil behaves.

Each soil type behaves in its own individual way, so you will need to experiment with the local soil before 'following up' a trail. Also, some soils can give a false impression of the size of the track: for example, tracks appear larger than life in sand and smaller than life in heavy clay.

Practice

Putting all this information together is actually much easier than it appears. The secret is constant practice: once you have used and learned a technique, you will never forget it.

The next stage in your training programme is to go back to the beginning and practise the skills we have shown you again, but paying much greater attention to detail and constantly estimating the tracks' age.

Tracking exercises

When you have difficulty finding the next track, study the last visible track. Contained within its complex nuances are the clues that will point to the next track.

Find a stretch of clear ground, ideally a sandy beach, and with a team-mate lay down sets of tracks to represent different activities and styles of movement. Draw all of the tracks as a pattern. Then study each track individually, paying careful attention to the way in which the slight nuances indicate the direction and distance of the next track.

Select specific experiments from the notes you made of the last exercise and repeat them under more testing conditions. This will show you how the damp sand reflected detail much more clearly than other soils.

Pick a fresh animal trail, or lay your own trail, and observe it at three-hourly intervals until the trail vanishes. Repeat this under as many different weather and soil conditions as possible.

Repeat the previous exercise but cover three of the tracks with upturned plastic containers. As the trail ages, gradually remove the containers and note the difference in detail of the tracks. Repeat this exercise under as many different circumstances as possible. By labelling the tracks with dated lolly sticks, you will have a graphic representation of the ageing of tracks.

Follow an animal trail as far as you can. Do not be put off: find every track, and persevere. By now you should be fairly proficient.

Bruise various stems on different types of vegetation and note the differing details as they age. Always leave one plant undamaged to act as a control.

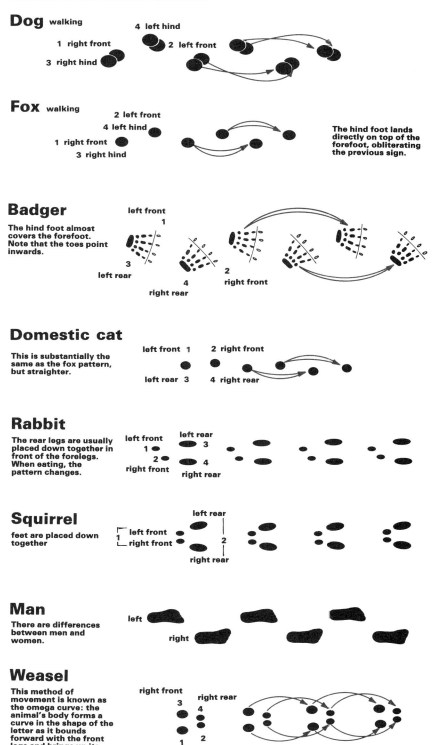

How animals move

Each group of animals moves in a different way: they move different foot combinations, and to further complicate the issue they move in different patterns at different speeds. The numbers indicate which foot hits the ground first. The only way to learn more about these animals is through first-hand tracking experience and careful observation of the animal in its natural habitat.

Dog walking

1 right front
2 left front
3 right hind
4 left hind

Fox walking

1 right front
2 left front
3 right hind
4 left hind

The hind foot lands directly on top of the forefoot, obliterating the previous sign.

Badger

The hind foot almost covers the forefoot. Note that the toes point inwards.

1 left front
2 right front
3 left rear
4 right rear

Domestic cat

This is substantially the same as the fox pattern, but straighter.

1 left front
2 right front
3 left rear
4 right rear

Rabbit

The rear legs are usually placed down together in front of the forelegs. When eating, the pattern changes.

1 left front
2 right front
3 left rear
4 right rear

Squirrel

feet are placed down together

1 left front
1 right front
2 right rear
left rear

Man

There are differences between men and women.

left
right

Weasel

This method of movement is known as the omega curve: the animal's body forms a curve in the shape of the letter as it bounds forward with the front legs and brings up its rear legs.

3 right front
4 right rear
1 left front
2 left rear

Tracking: The follow-up

Asking questions

You can gain valuable information about your target from the locals and from your own troops. Here are some useful questions to help you build up a picture of the enemy:

1. Who was he/were they?
2. What was he/were they wearing?
3. What unit did they belong to?
4. How did they look?
5. Were they armed? If so, what with?
6. What have the local weather conditions been like since they were seen?
7. What were they doing when you saw them?
8. Where might they have been going?
9. What was their average age?
10. What sex were they?
11. How tall were they?
12. How heavy were they?
13. What sort of build were they?
14. What was their hair colour/length/type?
15. Where were they last seen?

The rotor blades clatter above, imposing an unnatural silence on your team-mates and giving you the chance for mental preparation. As tracker, the success or failure of the operation will be on your shoulders. You think through the devious ploys you have encountered and remember the many mistakes you made in training.

After what seems like an eternity the chopper banks. The side door slides back, revealing the perfect tracking light of dawn.

The 'point of last contact'

On arrival at the PLC you will be under pressure to begin the follow-up immediately. But without the correct preparation this can prove disastrous. If the track is 'very hot' (fresh), it may be feasible to follow up straight away if there are several tracking teams: while one team follows up, the other teams can gather the relevant intelligence. But solo tracking without preparation is suicidal: do so only under what *you* judge to be exceptional circumstances.

Basic pre-follow up preparations

Time spent gathering information is never wasted. But remember that the weather will not wait for you: it is already at work, smoothing away the 'sign'.

1 Secure the vicinity of PLC

The greatest technical problem you are likely to face is finding the trail. Normally by the time you arrive, the areas has been flattened by the feet of 'friendly forces'! As soon as you get there, the PLC area and its surroundings should be made off-limits to all but the trackers and their cover groups.

Dawn, and the start of a counter-terrorist operation for the South African Defence Force. Inserting the tracking team by air means they arrive in the area fresh and do not run the risk of mine attack on the roads.

These are the remains of a Viet Cong who managed to evade the follow-up after being wounded in an ambush by the Australian Special Air Service.

Those of you who drop rubbish on exercise are asking for trouble, and burying it under stones will not go unnoticed by the tracker. Give as little information away as possible: your rubbish will speak volumes.

2 Set up an operational HQ

Commanders using tracking teams should establish a forward support HQ, near the area of operation to reduce transportation delays. Apart from normal military considerations, the HQ must provide the following tracker support:

Radio communications.

Transportation, capable of inserting tracker teams ahead of the target, ideally helicopters.

Photocopiers or Polaroid cameras, to distribute photos or drawing of target tracks.

3 Gather intelligence

The usual difficulty is not in finding sign, but in distinguishing your target's sign from normal disturbances. Even in remote areas paths are used regularly by the local population. The more you know about the target, the easier this task will be.

Develop close liaison with the Intelligence Officer. He will be able to give you valuable information, such as what the enemy ration wrappers look like, what footwear they use, and so on. When the operation is over you will hold a debrief to enhance the picture of the enemy.

The IO's information is invaluable, but more up-to-date information can be obtained by interviewing the troops or civilians who have had the most recent contact with the target/s. Take care: if you ask leading questions you run the risk of influencing the subject's reply. If you ask a village about jungle terrorists, for example, you should ask: "What was their footwear?" You are likely to receive an accurate answer, ranging from "none" to "jungle boots". But if you ask, "What boots were they wearing? 'you

are influencing the answer, and if they cannot remember you may even fool yourself into believing they *are* wearing boots.

The fast 'follow up'

As soon as possible, organize a search for the trail. If you are the only tracker, you will have to follow the trail faster than it was made. Most teams begin by dividing the tasks: one or two teams may cut for sign in a circle around the PLC, while others might cut along the edges of paths, roads or rivers in the area.

Once the trail has been found, the clock really begins to tick. With the general direction of the target's movement identified, the search teams can concentrate their effort in a narrow corridor. The team that has the trail 'tapes' their start point and begins following up.

Meanwhile, the other teams begin to cut across the search corridor some distance ahead of the follow-up team. If one of these teams discovers the trail they begin following up, and the first follow-up team leap frogs past them to 'cut ahead'. In this way the distance between trackers and target is reduced very rapidly.

Live tracking

As you round the bend in the track, something catches your eye: there is some darkness around the base of a rock, perhaps, showing that it has been moved. Carefully examining the surrounding area, you find the trail. There is no room for mistakes now. First of all, radio in your position and the details of the trail as you see it: number the targets, speed of travel etc. HQ will be able to tell you whether your information corresponds to pre-

Tactical tracking sequence: the tracking team find sign of terrorist movement. Team commanders discuss the track and decide what they are going to be dealing with.

The first team then follows the spore step-by-step and puts out flank protection. All information on the enemy being picked up by the tracker is radioed back.

The second team pushes forward to see if it can pick up the trail ahead of the first team. Take care that the overbounding group does not destroy sign.

Closing the net

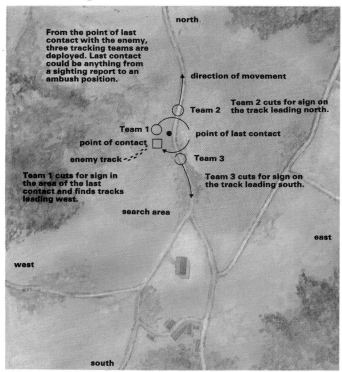

From the point of last contact with the enemy, three tracking teams are deployed. Last contact could be anything from a sighting report to an ambush position.

north

direction of movement

Team 2 cuts for sign on the track leading north.

Team 2

Team 1

point of last contact

point of contact

enemy track

Team 3

Team 1 cuts for sign in the area of the last contact and finds tracks leading west.

Team 3 cuts for sign on the track leading south.

search area

east

west

south

1 This is known as the fast follow-up, and usually requires three teams of trackers of at least three men each. The tracking teams will also require protection of perhaps a half section, depending on the level of threat.

Teams 2 and 3 turn west and overbound ahead of team 1 in an attempt to cut sign.

Team 2 now picks up sign of enemy movement and follows up. The team on the trail of the enemy will constantly update the teams on the radio net, including the quick reaction force, on the enemy situation.

point of contact

2

Point of contact with enemy track

Team 1 follows up the trail left by the enemy and warns off HQ and the other teams, telling them to turn west.

1

3

Once both teams are ahead of team 1 they cut across team 1's line of advance to cut track.

Search area

2 Team 1 follows the trail from where they picked it up at the point of last contact. Teams 2 and 3, having searched in an area north and south respectively for the track, both turn west and continue cutting for sign.

vious info. It may be that the enemy group have split up or joined a larger force.

Next, mark the trail using coloured tape so that another tracker team will know the trail has been discovered, or so that you can easily resume tracking the next day.

Estimate the age of the trail, and keeping an eye on this factor: it will enable you to judge whether or not you are gaining ground. Your life may well hang on this thin thread of data.

From now on you must be alert to all that is going on around you. Make sure the cover group understand that they are your eyes and ears while you are concentrating on the trail. Be as silent as possible, use hand signals to communicate, and at all costs keep the radio from bursting out or crackling. Tracking is tiring, so it's not a bad idea to take a rest ever 10 minutes or, better still, rotate point duty with another tracker.

As you close the distance, make sure to keep your cover group informed, otherwise they may not be alert, which will put all your lives at risk. Tracking is like reeling in a fish: you have to be careful not to move too fast. Gradually close in on the target until you establish visual contact (binoculars can be useful here), and radio in their exact location. It is here

that your task will normally end, with the deployment of a fire force.

When the operation is over there wil be a debrief. You may be able to shed some light on the enemy's SOP, and the tracking team will hopefully be allowed some rest. Expect no glory for tracking!

In South Africa the tracking teams are supported by Ratel APCs, with the trackers running ahead of the vehicles and the relief tracker and protection troops being carried in the Ratel.

Successful tracking

It is not enough just to follow the clues left behind by the target. You must interpret those signs to gain an understanding of the target's movements so that you can predict his movements or his aim.

If the target is expecting to be tracked, he may be planning to ambush you or lay a booby-trap. Only your tracking skill can help you here. Caution, careful interpretation and a steady tracking pace are your allies: tiredness, carelessly taking signs at face value, and undue haste along the trail can be fatal enemies.

As you follow the trail, pay attention to all types of sign, not just the tracks. Stop to look around and listen every few paces: trackers are frequently shot because they spend too long looking at the ground! By looking up and studying the direction in which the target is moving you will gain a better appreciation of why the tracks are being made the way they are.

Try to pay equal attention to the ground on each side of the trail: you may detect sign that indicates the target is aware of your presence. Suspect everything. If you come across evidence such as dropped or discarded equipment, treat it as a probable booby-trap.

Try to avoid destroying the 'sign' you have just followed, and never pass beyond a sign until you can see the next sign. If you cannot find the next track, pay careful attention to the last visible sign: the lines of force should indicate where a track lies. Use your tracking stick to help you, and make sure that the track has not been obliterated because of freak conditions. If you still cannot find the next sign, check left or right of the trail. If that doesn't work, read the pattern of the last few tracks: do they indicate any change in pace or direction?

The last resort before 'cutting ahead' is to check near and far from the last sign. If you are using a tracking stick and are positioned to make the best use of available light, you will not often lose the trail. Remember: the key to successful tracking is practice.

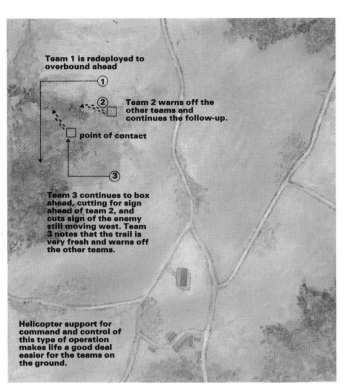

Team 1 is redeployed to overbound ahead

Team 2 warns off the other teams and continues the follow-up.

point of contact

Team 3 continues to box ahead, cutting for sign ahead of team 2, and cuts sign of the enemy still moving west. Team 3 notes that the trail is very fresh and warns off the other teams.

Helicopter support for command and control of this type of operation makes life a good deal easier for the teams on the ground.

3 Team 2 has cut sign and warns the other groups by radio. Team 1 stops tracking, mounts up on its transport and is redeployed to cover north and west of Team 2. Meanwhile, Team 3 has cut sign.

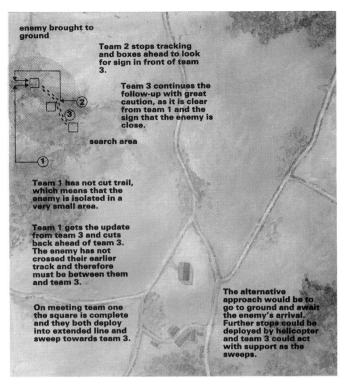

enemy brought to ground

Team 2 stops tracking and boxes ahead to look for sign in front of team 3.

Team 3 continues the follow-up with great caution, as it is clear from team 1 and the sign that the enemy is close.

search area

Team 1 has not cut trail, which means that the enemy is isolated in a very small area.

Team 1 gets the update from team 3 and cuts back ahead of team 3. The enemy has not crossed their earlier track and therefore must be between them and team 3.

On meeting team one the square is complete and they both deploy into extended line and sweep towards team 3.

The alternative approach would be to go to ground and await the enemy's arrival. Further stops could be deployed by helicopter and team 3 could act with support as the sweeps.

4 Team 3 continues the follow-up. 1 and 2 cut ahead. Team 2 cuts the trail of the target and Team 3, and so boxes ahead. On meeting Team 1, they know the enemy is between them and Team 3, and so they cut back.

Other uses of trackers

Trackers have a unique balance of skills and they can prove ideal scouts for raiding parties and long-range recce patrols. If they're good shots they can be first-class snipers.

In a training capacity, trackers will prove very useful in highlighting mistakes in camouflage and sloppy fieldcraft, generally uplifting a whole unit's ability.

Left: Paratroopers can be used when tracking down large groups of terrorists, as they can be dropped as a killer group ahead of the terrorists' line of march.

Above: South African Defence Force soldiers debus under cover of 50-calibre fire. Motor transport allows you to put in heavily armed 'stops' at speed.

Fighting Fit

Course members look on as the outdoor exit trainer is demonstrated by the staff. The kit simulates the slipstream of the aircraft and the pull of the canopy opening.

What it takes to be a Para
KNACKER CRACKER

The 'knacker cracker', as the Outdoor Exit Trainer is commonly known, simulates exiting an aircraft into the slipstream. It is also designed to provide a feeling of the tug caused by your deploying parachute, followed by the descent itself. Nothing can compare with the real thing, of course, but as a training aid the OET gives you a fair idea of what to expect. It also provides the PJIs with a good opportunity to observe your exit position.

The OET is a raised, enclosed platform with a doorway on each side.

Harnesses are suspended from several cables, which extend from each door to strong points a short distance in front of, and at a lower level than, the tower. After mounting a stairway to the platform you wait your turn to get into a harness before launching yourselves, one at a time, through the designated doorway.

Drilling with loads

You all experienced the OET just prior to your initial (clean fatigue) jump. Now the drills are carried out with a container strapped to your front, below the reserve parachute.

As soon as you leave the doorway you drop a couple of metres before your fall is abruptly checked. The pull of the uncomfortable leg straps raises your voice an octave or two (hence the nickname!). 'One thousand, two thousand, three thousand!' The words are squeezed out of you by the sudden tightening of the harness. Your eyes are still watering as you stop bouncing and begin hurtling down towards the end of the cable.

A couple of your mates grab your feet, stopping you from travelling

1074

**The badge of
The Parachute Regiment**

Above: As you approach the water you bin your container and then the reserve chute, struggle out of the harness, sit in the bum strap until your feet touch, then jump. Hopefully you will then avoid a watery grave.

Main picture: If you are dropped over water there is a good chance that you will drown if you hit the water with kit and still attached to the harness. Part of the drill involves getting out of the leg loops in preparation for jumping out of the harness.

further and allowing you to carry out the flight drills as taught. You release the container and finally slip out of the harness as if you are coming in for a water landing. Then up you all go for another attempt! What fun!

The following day sees your first container descent, followed that evening by a (clean fatigue) night drop. Most of you dread jumping in darkness, but the night descent will probably be the softest landing you are likely to make.

Admittedly, waiting in the aircraft before the jump is somewhat unnerving. After standing and hooking up, the Number One in the stick finds himself waiting in the door for what seems an eternity. You try not to look down, but it is impossible not to notice the tiny lights twinkling far below. Outside, all else is blackness.

A minute ticks by. You are aware of the cold, buffeting wind blowing into your face and tugging at your clothing. You must have been waiting at least a couple of minutes now. When the hell are you going to jump? Much more of this and . . . Red on! At last. Okay, any moment now, any moment . . . Nothing happens! Bloody hell! The seconds pass. What's the delay?

'Green on!'

What?

'Go!'

Count. Your parachute cracks open. Check! Okay. All-round observation. Fine! Hey, what's that below? Another 'chute? How can that be? You were first out the door. How did another parachutist get underneath you? You are engrossed by the pale circle below. It gets bigger and bigger. Why isn't he dropping at the same rate as you?

You are still staring when you suddenly hit the ground, landing alongside the round sandpit. Not a parachute after all. Because it's dark and you don't see the ground-rush, most of you are relaxed as you come in so you hardly notice the landing. Great!

But two men are unlucky. One man-

The last man in the stick lugs his burden to the door. When carrying a full combat load and ammo, the most painful part of the trip is usually the time spent trying to stand up with a Bergen tied to your legs, a reserve on your chest and the main chute on your back.

On the route out for the night jump. These are never a big favourite as it is difficult to assess your drift or see fences, trees, other chutes and anything else that will really hurt.

ages to damage both ankles. Another, the soldier who joined the Platoon during Week One at Brize Norton, injures one ankle. The rest of you survive unscathed.

The time arrives for your eighth, qualifying, jump. By now you are quite used to the routine. DFC . . . The short walk out to the waiting Hercules . . . The delay as you strap yourselves into your seats . . . The familiar sounds as the big aircraft surges forward and

lifts into the air ... Many of you are nonchalant and pretend to catch a few minutes of shut-eye. Not for long.

'Port stick, prepare for action!'

You 'wake up', undo your seat belt and lengthen the straps, as shown. You place one foot through the container leg strap before attaching the jettison device. Then the instructors carry out their interim check.

'Stand up. Fit equipment. Hook up!'

You stand and turn outboard, fit the container and tighten the leg strap. You snap on the reserve and finally clip your static line to the overhead steel cable.

'Check equipment!'

The routine is always the same. First, you examine the strop and static-line hook, making sure that both are secure and that there are no twists. Check that your helmet is fastened correctly. Make sure that both D-rings on your reserve are okay. Lift the reserve, bang the QRF and check the T-bar. Fine.

Check the man in front

Make sure that equipment hooks are facing outwards. Check the jettison device and leg strap. Finally, examine the man in front: his strop, helmet and the three visible ties on the back of his parachute pack. The last man in the stick then turns outboard to be checked by the man to his front.

'Tell off for equipment check.'

Each of you lets the instructor know you have been satisfactorily checked, down to the last man.

'One okay. Port stick okay!'

The instructor/despatcher checks everyone and then brings you to Action Stations. You wait patiently, first man in the door, left foot forward, left hand over the door. The red light blinks on. Here we go again ... Arm down to grasp the wrist of the hand gripping the container handle.

The stick exits the Hercules, the static line snapping the canopies open as you exit. The route in is always a bit rough as the pilot avoids notional ground fire approaching the DZ.

'Green on ... GO!'

Carry out the drills and finally release the container jettison device allowing the container to fall to the end of its five-metre line. Minutes later you are on *terra firma*, having technically just become a paratrooper!

If time and weather permit, you will carry out one more descent before leaving Brize Norton. The operational descent, although not strictly neces-

You must be able to get out of your harness as soon as you hit the deck. The canopy may not collapse on landing and could drag you along the ground, so collapse by pulling in the rigging lines on one side.

Once you have a piece of sky to yourself, check round and then release your container. This then acts as an anchor in the sky and reduces your drift.

sary, is one that the RAF likes to conduct. It is similar to the drops you have already made but it is carried out onto an 'operational DZ', usually on Salisbury Plain.

Afterwards you are formed up and awarded the coveted parachute wings. During this 'wings parade' you will also receive a formal warning regarding your new status. The Green Light Warning Order is your final chance to decide whether you really want to be a paratrooper. Should any of you refuse to jump after accepting your wings, you can be courtmartialled! Of course, none of you have any doubts whatsoever. All of you have sewed on your wings days ago!

Combat Report
Rhodesia:
Guerrilla Ambush near Mkumbura

A member of Grey's Scouts in the Rhodesian Army describes a guerrilla ambush near the border with Mozambique.

We had been told to report to Inkomo Barracks at 6 and to be ready to move out by 7 a.m. The trucks were packed and we were ready to go, but we were still sitting there at 10 when the OC, Lieutenant Nell, eventually turned up. He had come from the army HQ in Salisbury and his briefing had taken longer than expected. It was 10.15 a.m. before we were on our way.

We were to operate in the Mkumbura area, close to the Mozambique border, in support of a combat engineer squad. Our unit, the mounted infantry, had a good relationship with the engineers as we had worked together on the cordon sanitaire, laying mines in the Penhalonga and Inyanga areas on the eastern border.

After several stops at the troopie canteens we eventually hit Mount Darwin around 4 p.m. We were to spend the night there, in Indian country, as it was too late to travel to Mkumbura. We were to sleep by the swimming pool, next to which was a bar. Naturally that's where we spent the evening, chatting to some commando troops who were on Fire Force duty.

The sound of small-arms fire

We moved out next morning at 8 a.m., a three-hour journey still ahead of us. I was in the first truck with Sergeant Patrick, a former member of the French paras; Corporal Crooks, ex-British Army; three Rhodesians from the Territorial Force; and four African soldiers. Being in the first truck was great: it meant you didn't have to eat dust the whole time.

We had gone about 30 km when suddenly our truck hit a mine. I swear I never heard the explosion. All I can recall is the truck going up and down like a roller coaster, with rocks and dust flying everywhere. Next there was the sound of small-arms fire. We debussed, having suffered no casualties apart from our driver, who had broken his ankle.

The guys from the other trucks were already returning fire. Apparently an RPG rocket had just missed the second truck. We couldn't see the targets, but just hoped that our rate of fire would make the terrorists keep their heads

down. Fortunately they were shooting high, despite being on a hill.

By now we had got over the initial shock and were getting our act together. The OC was reporting the contact to Mount Darwin in the hope of calling up Fire Force. Corporal Crooks and a TF trooper got the commando mortar into action, as did Trooper Bobbie Clark, an ex-Green Jacket who was in the third truck. Eight rounds later, the firing from the hill had died down.

They were running away

Led by Sergeant Patrick, we left our positions and moved up the hill for a counter-attack. On the way we found one wounded terrorist, on whom our medic soon got to work, and one dead terrorist. The rest were all running away, firing their AKs over their shoulders as they went. We found out later from the wounded terrorist that there had been about 30 of them split into two groups.

Lieutenant Nell, who had managed to get through to Mount Darwin, was giving Fire Force the direction of the fleeing terrorists and also asking for casevac, as two of our national servicemen were wounded besides our driver. My section did a sweep of the area, picking up two SKSs and one AK dropped by the fleeing terrorists.

Then one of our African soldiers spotted a blood spoor leading away from the contact area into some thick bush. Sergeant Patrick reported this by radio to Lieutenant Nell. Orders came back to check it out. Led by one of the Africans, five of us followed the spoor. We got within a hundred metres of the bush when a terrorist opened up. We hit the dirt and returned fire. Then Corporal Crooks fired his Zulu. There was a dull thump. We waited. There was no return fire.

No return fire

Three of us knelt and fired into the bush. Again, no return fire. We all stood up and moved in an extended line towards the target. About a metre into the bush I came across what looked like a bundle of rags.

I called Sergeant Patrick over. The terrorist must have been hit by one of our first bursts of fire; he had been cut to pieces. The Zulu had

An Alouette lifts off. The Rhodesian airmobile effort was a shoestring operation but proved very useful for quick reaction.

missed by miles. We gave him a quick search, and found five dollars. We picked up his SKS and went back down the hill. Overhead the Fire Force choppers hovered, and in the distance we could see the K-Car chopper in action.

We got back to the road just as a chopper was taking off with the two wounded national servicemen and the wounded terrorist. The driver had to go back to Mount Darwin with us, as there was no room for him in the chopper.

Lieutenant Nell chose volunteers to stay with the truck that had hit a mine. A repair team plus two trucks was on its way. We, the lucky ones, headed back to Mount Darwin.

The Rhodesian Army had a good many ex-British Army personnel plus a fair number of Americans and a few Frenchmen fighting alongside the Rhodesians.

Left: Some of the trackers from Grey's Scouts taking it easy by the pool.

Fighting Fit

The badge of
The Parachute Regiment

What it takes to be a Para
THE FINAL FENCE

After Brize Norton, no time is lost in preparing for your final field exercise. "Last Fence" is scheduled to begin on Sunday of Week 21. Weather permitting, you will parachute into the exercise on this, your first tactical drop. The familiar weighted container is to be replaced by a practical CSPEP/Bergen. In the run-up to D-Day, you draw and prepare this and other equipment required for the four-day period. You are also provided with a detailed briefing by the Platoon Commander. For

the purpose of Last Fence, the Salisbury Plain Training Area has been renamed Salania, and represents a fictitious island in northern Europe . . .

"Salania has maintained a good relationship with Britain since being liberated by our forces at the end of the Second World War. Although presently under a Socialist government, Salania is politically split by factions loyal to the Western Democratic countries which flank its northern and western shores, and those to the Communist countries to the south and

east . . .

"For many years the major industries have revolved around the mineral and ore mining areas of west Salania. Recently, however, oil was discovered off the east coast . . .

The battle picture

"Visbij, the capital, is situated in the centre of the country, on what is known as the east-west divide. Just outside the capital is the airport, serving both civil and military authorities. While western Salania is the main

first tactical drop onto Salisbury [Plai]n at last light is what it's all about: [ther]e is no better way to start an exercise [than] with the adrenalin rush of a [night] drop.

The Wings Parade: young paras, looking suitably pleased and relieved, receive the famous Wings badge, the blue badge of courage. Now they are part of the Maroon Mafia, the Airborne Brotherhood.

cattle, and fenced-off areas for growing crops such as barley and corn. Rough tracks make the plains largely unsuitable for ordinary vehicles – most of those used are farm vehicles with good ground clearance and four-wheel drive capability . . .

"The only metalled roads are those entering the capital. The main road runs from the northern Port of Vårö, south-east through Visbij, and south to the Port of Valdisk. There is also a major road running almost parallel from Vårö, down through the industrial town of Zlite and in to the capital some six kilometres further east. Zlite is the housing and administrative centre for the oilfield work force . . .

The enemy situation

"A new organisation calling itself the Salanian People's Action Committee is claiming that the discovery of oil will have a detrimental effect on the export of the country's minerals, ore and agricultural produce. SPAC, as the organisation is known, has won over a large element of the mainly peasant local defence force. Many have broken away to form a military wing whose members have kidnapped the British Director of the Independent Drilling and Exploration Company tasked with the offshore exploration programme . . .

Pulling out

"Furthermore, SPAC has taken over some of IDECO's homesteads, demanding that the oil company pulls out of Salania. It is believed that SPAC is supported financially and militarily by the eastern bloc, and unconfirmed Intelligence reports indicate that terrorist-trained advisors are now heading SAU-type groups in the country . . .

"You have been ordered to southern Norway, where you will remain

Having hit the deck and checked that your arms and legs still work, rope in the container and get to your weapon. The SA80 is a far better weapon than the SLR for Paras.

on immediate standby . . ."

Meanwhile, back in the real world, you are scheduled to drop in to Salisbury Plain at 1100 hrs on Sunday. Unfortunately, on the day the Met Office reports winds gusting up to 28 knots, increasing as the day goes on. The forecast results in the platoon having to wait on standby at RAF Lyneham. In the meantime, the platoon sergeant drives out to the DZ, and is surprised to find perfect weather conditions: no wind, and excellent visibility! He decides to make a few phone calls. Consequently, the drop is re-scheduled for 1530 hrs that afternoon, providing the weather doesn't deteriorate.

At last you board the C-130. Shortly after take-off, an announcement is broadcast over the aircraft tannoy

A break for scoff. Watch out when using hexamine in enclosed spaces like buildings and trenches. On exercise, eat at every chance you get, which may not necessarily match a normal mealtime.

industrial region, the east is dedicated toward the agricultural economy.

"From these facts it is clear that the poorer half of the community is concentrated in the east. Although a great percentage of workers also inhabit the west, the east has developed into the stronghold of extreme left-wing politics . . .

"East Salania is largely an open land with scattered homesteads. Its undulating terrain is dotted with small copses or wooded areas, not all of which are marked on existing maps. There are also tracts of land for grazing

When you've evicted the enemy from some farm buildings there is time for a brew, among the weapon cleaning, ammo redistribution and dealing with casualties and prisoners.

The SA80 has an excellent comprehensive cleaning kit, seen here being put to good use. The smaller calibre of the SA80 should make it more sensitive than the SLR, but stoppages are rare.

system. You are informed that due to a complete breakdown in talks and as a result of increased belligerence by SPAC, the Salanian government has been forced to outlaw the dissident movement. Because of the increased danger now faced by the British and American employees of IDECO, it has been decided that you will spearhead a rescue operation.

Evacuation area

Your task is to secure the area around Zlite for the imminent evacuation of IDECO personnel. The announcement provides additional realism to the occasion, and even gets a cheer from the platoon. Shortly afterwards, the Hercules approaches the DZ, and at 1530 hrs the first man throws himself through the door.

The aircraft makes only one pass. Over Salania, the darkening sky quickly fills with parachutists. Within a couple of minutes the entire platoon is safely on the ground and hurriedly forming up under section corporals. Order is rapidly established, whereupon each section moves off in the direction of a wooded hill.

Contact!

You aren't certain what to expect, but have the feeling that something is bound to happen soon. It does. Suddenly: contact! One of the sections comes under fire from a single rifleman. The incident lasts only a few seconds before the enemy breaks off and disappears into the woods. The woods! Well, that's obviously going to be the first objective.

You clear it in a text-book attack, using the lessons of fire and manoeuvre perfected during Advanced Wales.

Documents found on the "dead" identify them as specialist troops. They are dressed in an unusual camouflage pattern and wear sky-blue berets! Their weapons, probably sup-

plied to Salania by Britain in the not so distant past, are the same as your own. You take the opportunity to seize a quantity of ammunition for your own use. A paratrooper soon learns to be self-sufficient if he is to remain operationally effective.

After reorganising, you quietly move out of the wood and tab a short distance before establishing a harbour position. Throughout this first night the platoon conducts a number of reconnaissance missions upon a nearby hamlet.

In the early hours of a freezing cold, November morning you find yourself part of a group crawling towards an abandoned house. It is one of five double-storey buildings grouped around a single-storey structure. The empty building looks as though it might provide a suitable OP and, what's more, it's out of the wind!

A window on the ground floor looks out towards the other houses. Perfect! It is soon confirmed that the place is being used by an enemy unit. They have apparently made their HQ in the centre building, where the majority seem to be gathered. A log fire has been built against an outside wall. Around the corner, a four-ton truck has been backed up so that it might be

While the platoon rests, the sentries armed with the LSWs keep watch in pairs. The blank firing attachment does tend to compromise the sentry's position.

mistaken in the dark for an extension of the building.

You remain hidden for as long as it takes to determine how many enemy are present, and the location of their billets. There seem to be at least half a dozen soldiers — some in the centre building, others in a house beyond. When you finally move out you have a very good idea of the camp layout.

Specific tasks

At 0730 hrs on Monday morning the platoon launches its attack. Each section has been briefed for a specific task, and you operate smoothly and efficiently in conjunction with each other. The six houses are individually cleared by grenade and rifle and automatic fire. It is done quickly, with the minimum of fuss. Any enemy inside is killed. You take no chances, employing the aggressive techniques learned during house-clearing in Wales.

Smoke and explosions

One or two of the buildings catch fire, filling the air with acrid black smoke. It mingles with the coloured smoke from numerous grenades. Explosions and reports reverberate against stone walls. Above it all can be heard authoritative shouts of command. You respond automatically. When told to fire, you aim and squeeze the trigger. When ordered to cease firing, you stop. When given the command to move, you move.

The area is secured in minutes. Each section is allocated one or two buildings, and sentries are deployed. The rest of you settle down out of the chill and busy yourselves with the task of cleaning weapons and re-arming from the stocks of ammunition discovered amongst the enemy supplies. Water bottles are replenished from a number of jerrycans found in the HQ block. There are even fresh eggs for a lucky few.

Combat Report
Lebanon:
Druze Retaliation in Beirut

The author was serving with the French Foreign Legion in 1983 when part of his unit was deployed to Beirut.

Yasser Arafat had appealed to the French government to send forces to Beirut to protect Palestinian families in the refugee camps. When we arrived I was attached to the 6th Company of 2e Regiment Estrangere d'Infanterie.

During the first couple of weeks there was a stand-off period as the Druze militiamen sussed out our positions. There was the odd snipe and rocket attack, but we were well dug in and very alert.

Then, one day, French aircraft from the carrier Clemenceau attacked Druze positions. The first retaliation came in around tea-time – just a couple of RPG-7s, more of an annoyance than anything else. That evening there was a full stand-to. I was in a bunker by the front gate dressed in a flak jacket and steel helmet. We had a 0.5-in Browning machine-gun and boxes of ammunition, so we were ready, although I didn't know what for.

Around about 10 o'clock that evening, a salvo of artillery shells landed in front of the camp. They didn't cause any damage, but they hit a house opposite. Some of our men went to help dig out the injured and the rest of the night was relatively quiet.

They hit the vehicles

I came off stag at midnight and slept like a log until eight the next morning. I had been tasked to go in a convoy to the French embassy, leaving at 10 o'clock. The vehicles were already lined up by 9.30 but suddenly there came the whistling of an artillery shell on its way in. I didn't need anyone to tell me to take cover: I was in a slit trench before the shell hit the ground, and as others followed the trench was soon pretty packed. We untangled ourselves and looked around to see if we could move somewhere else. Some of the men made a run for it, easing the congestion a little.

All the time the shells were crashing into the compound, throwing up huge clouds of dust. During a lull we all left the trench and headed

The evening sky lit up by shellfire as military artillery fires into Beirut. In spite of this the Druze guns were still pounding us in 1983.

for better cover. I got into a bunker near the front gate and sat down to wait for it to stop, but it got worse! I wouldn't like to guess how many shells came in, but there was explosion after explosion.

The bunker soon became very stuffy, and I was beginning to get well pissed off with all the noise. The Druze OP must have been in a good position, because they were bracketing the whole area in the compound. They must have zeroed in when they fired the night before.

It wasn't too long before they hit the vehicles. One shell went through the hatch of an AML-90, setting off the ammunition inside, and it continued to explode throughout the day. Every time we thought it had stopped we tried to get to the other vehicles to move them, as one by one they were beginning to catch fire. We failed each time, so our sergeant told us to forget them and stay under cover.

In the afternoon the artillery bombardment slackened off, but the compound came under attack from rocket and small-arms fire. The militiamen had used the bombardment to get round the compound in order to attack us. We fired back, and soon my ears were ringing with the noise.

I watched as the rounds I was firing took huge chunks out of the building opposite. If there were any men in there, I bet they kept their heads down. They kept firing for about two hours, then it slackened off and the heavy stuff started again. This gave them the chance to get themselves, and any dead or wounded, out of the area.

When the bombardment started up again it caught some men in the open. One guy, Daugey, was hit outside our bunker and crashed against the door. We hurriedly pulled him inside. He was moaning, and was peppered with shrapnel down his back. He seemed in a bad way, but the blood made it look worse than it was. As we only had field dressings with us we decided to carry him to the hospital dugout. This was only about 80 metres away, but with the shells coming down it looked a very long 80 metres.

We waited for a gap in the shelling, then off we went. Just as we got there a shell came whistling down. We all dived for the door and landed in a great big heap on top of Daugey, breaking his arm in the process. We didn't know

this at the time: we thought he was complaining about his wounds again.

Once everything had settled down, we got him inside and laid him face down on a table. A doctor came over and gave him a quick once-over, then two medics set about cutting his uniform off. He was given an injection, which must have done the trick, as he stopped moaning and started grinning.

We couldn't go out again because of the shelling, so I took a look around the dugout. It was just like a scene from MASH. There were six tables and each had a wounded man on it. At the far end of the dugout there was a body covered by a poncho: all I could see was the feet sticking out. A medic came pushing by and told me to get out of the way. We decided to make a run for it by leap-frogging from bunker to bunker.

I went first, and ran like hell to the nearest trench. Then I looked for the next position. The main building was nearby. I took off for it and headed straight for the cellars, the safest place. They also kept out most of the noise, although they were stuffy and dusty.

A shell slammed into the side

I stayed down there for about four hours. The shelling continued the whole time. I managed to get something to eat, but just picked at the food. When an officer came in and asked for volunteers to take over the bunker on the roof, my hand went up like a shot.

I went to the third floor and met another five blokes at the stairs. As we were climbing them a shell slammed into the side of the building, sending us all flying. Luckily, apart from shock and being covered in dust, we were all fine. We went up on to the roof and relieved the other guys. They just nodded and shot off down the stairs. "We must be wearing the wrong aftershave," I said, to lighten the mood. No-one laughed, and I couldn't blame them.

Actually, it wasn't too bad on the roof, and after about an hour the shelling seemed to be wearing off. Our blokes were then able to move a bit more freely between bunkers, so they could be watered and fed. By about 9.45 there was just the occasional shell, and by 10 everything was quiet. We had one dead and 12 wounded, with injuries ranging from mild concussion to lost limbs.

The complete silence was really weird. I left the bunker and looked down into the compound. The AML was still burning, and in the early morning light it looked strangely beautiful.

An hour later we were relieved ourselves and taken to the cookhouse for scoff and then, hopefully, some rest. I hope I never have to spend another day like that again. It doesn't do the nerves any good!

The recce patrol is led by a recruit. He moves cautiously forward, leading from the front. In a small patrol like this it is sensible for the patrol commander to be the radio operator as well.

What it takes to be a Para
THE FINAL FENCE (Part 2)

Later on Monday morning – Day 2 of Exercise 'Last Fence' – you and three mates are detailed to recce a bridge a couple of miles from your present location. The recce is to be conducted entirely by yourselves – an indication of the level of confidence the training staff now have in your abilities.

You move out at 1200 hrs. The predetermined route is through a convenient valley and so provides a fair degree of cover until you arrive within just a few hundred metres of the objective. Forced to abandon the dead ground, you climb the ploughed slope of the valley, quickly crossing an open track before reaching the shelter of a field's hedgerow. You follow the hedge-line towards a cross-roads situated just beyond the field.

During your final approach, the section commander calls a number of halts to allow him to visually check the terrain in relation to his map. When you reach the end of the field, he decides to push ahead with only the radioman. The rest of you are instructed to remain concealed until their return.

The two men break cover and dart over the road, leap a fence and sprint across an overgrown field. They arrive at another fence, beyond which can be seen a muddy track. They pause to catch their breath. So far, so good, they think.

Escapers spotted

However, an enemy patrol has spotted the pair during their dash and are now informing their commander. Meanwhile, your own commander has elected to crawl forward on his own in order to try to locate the

The badge of
The Parachute Regiment

The enemy is also out and about, and bumps your position. There is a brief fire fight and the enemy withdraw, too fast for your quick reaction force to prevent their escape.

The deliberate attack on the bridge goes well: the enemy have to withdraw without managing to blow it, and you storm across the bridge once the far bank has been secured.

Above: A recce patrol on the move, wary of ambush. Its aim is to recce a bridge to see if it is held by the enemy.
Inset: A Puma arrives in the night to airlift the platoon forward in preparation for close target recce and the attack. Its searchlight illuminates the LS for a second to confirm its location.

hears the metallic ring as cocking levers are pulled back and then released. Time to go!

As the section commander and radioman rejoin you, shots are heard from the direction of the bridge. The enemy chooses to engage you at a distance, however, allowing you to escape. Later in the afternoon you are surprised by a hit-and-run raid. Your own reaction is to send out a section to engage the enemy, firing from the cover of nearby woods.

Taken prisoner

As you approach, the attackers are seen to flee. One man, though, is slow off the mark and brought back as a prisoner. The incoming patrols is extremely pleased with itself as the worried-looking captive is pushed forward, hands clasped behind his head.

The unfortunate man is made to kneel down while a member of the platoon questions him. The prisoner says nothing. Suddenly he lunges at the interrogator, sending him spraw-

ling. Not for long. Amidst loud guffaws from all present, the embarrassed soldier quickly regains his feet and sprints after the prisoner.

They meet in the middle of a pool of filthy water to end up rolling around until both are dripping with mud. An NCO suppresses his laughter sufficiently to separate the pair. He forces the captive onto his belly, hands on head and legs spreadeagled, and then lectures the recruit on interrogation techniques.

Later, as the incident was not planned for in the exercise programme, the prisoner is allowed to 'escape'.

Meanwhile, a para battalion, having earlier landed east of your position, has successfully taken Visbij and its surrounds, so it is possible for the RAF and FAA to use the airport. That even-

A recruit approaches one of the enemy dead, keeping him well covered. Supposedly dead bodies have a strange habit of doing you damage every time you carry out a sloppy drill.

bridge, which he knows must be close by. He quickly negotiates the track and slithers into the long grass.

Arriving at the crest of a hill, he is presented with a clear view of the objective: the bridge, with a winding road, and woods bordering a river. A vehicle seems to be partially concealed in the woods, where the enemy presumably encamped. This is confirmed when two sentries are seen to leave the area and begin to cross the bridge. Suddenly, they cock their weapons! Even from his position high above, the section commander clearly

ing, a Puma arrives to lift the platoon forward for another series of patrols on the bridge recced earlier.

This time you work at night, in pairs, each of which approaches the objective from different directions. At least one group succeeds in crawling to within 50-75 metres of the sentries on the bridge itself.

As the weather might close in at any time, restricting the use of helicopters, the main roads must be kept open in case they are required. So the next morning the bridge is taken out by the platoon, allowing you to push on to Zlite. Very little now lies between you and the ultimate objective, except for isolated bands of die-hard fanatics. Later in the day you run into one of these groups during an advance.

Early contact

The incident comes as a surprise for everyone, especially the platoon commander – for SPAC has chosen to defend a piece of ground totally different to the expected one! So contact is initiated much earlier. Despite the initial confusion order is rapidly established, and the position cleared after a prolonged right-flanking attack.

The rest of the day is mostly uneventful, and by evening you are comfortably ensconced in your own little wood. At 2000 a sudden whoosh, followed by several airbursts, preceeds a lightning attack. Then a quick burst of fire, which you reply to. It's the muffled sound of a Land Rover engine which signals the enemy's escape. Silence descends over the wood.

A furious roar disrupts the quiet. Another raid? No, much worse. Three men from the same section have been found still inside their sleeping bags. Two slept through the entire attack! The other had the good grace to stick his rifle out and fire off a few shots. Their corporal is fuming: if they had done this in wartime they and their mates could easily have been killed.

He orders the whole section to kit up and then takes them on a 17-mile patrol. They don't get back until 0330 – seven and a half hours later.

For those just off the patrol it promises to be a long and tiring day: another bridge attack is scheduled for 0830 hrs. The bridge is the last enemy strongpoint before Zlite, so it is well defended and wired up for 'demolition'.

For the assault, 2 Section is detailed to work its way behind the objective, with the task of providing a cut-off group along the road leading from the bridge. In order to get into position the section must make a wide detour and cross a small footbridge downstream, having reconnoitred the route the previous night. One section will provide fire support from high ground in front of the bridge while 3 Section assaults from the right flank and along the riverbank.

At 0830 the attack goes in. Everything goes according to plan. As part of 3 Section you find yourself initially in the forefront of battle. You race for-

ward, methodically taking out enemy positions as you advance. The 'Salanians' conduct a fighting withdrawal, gradually pulling back across the bridge to prepared defensive positions.

The entire scene is one of running figures, flitting in and out of multicoloured smokescreens. Rifle and automatic fire is continuous. A sudden whoomph accompanies a dazzling explosion at one end of the bridge, and at the opposite end a bunker is taken out with a perfectly aimed grenade thrown from the far bank!

Across the river

More detonations erupt along the length of the bridge. Everything seems to be burning, sending clouds of dense smoke spiralling into the air. Shouts of command, a burst of fire, and you cross the river. A few of the defenders now take to their heels and run straight into the cut-off party. The sound of a prolonged firefight tells its own story!

None of the enemy surrenders. They continue with their futile struggle right until the bitter end. Perhaps if they had known that they were up against the Parachute Regiment . . .

At last, the position can be considered taken. The enemy dead are checked. Section Commanders call for the ammunition state. The platoon then goes firm at the bridgehead. The road to Zlite is open, and the hostages' safe future guaranteed!

Exercise 'Last Fence' is over.

The platoon commander reports back to the company on the successful taking of the bridge. He also sends details of dead and wounded and casevac required, and requests a replen of ammo.

You reorg on the enemy trenches, search their dead and hurriedly restuff your magazines. Any ammo the enemy has left is rapidly souvenired.